essential

assessment

Science

Key Stage 2

David Evans

STANLEY
THORNES

First published in 1997 by
Stanley Thornes Publishers Ltd
Ellenborough House
Wellington Street
Cheltenham
GL50 1YW

97 98 99 00 / 10 9 8 7 6 5 4 3 2 1

A catalogue record for this book is available from the British Library.

ISBN 0-7487-2875-9

Designed by Ian Foulis and Associates, Saltash, Cornwall

Printed and bound in Great Britain

Contents

These notes will help you use this book to the best advantage. They explain the ideas behind the book, the contents and the way the material can be used. Ultimately, however, it will be up to you to decide how to make use of the assessments.

The structure of the book

This book is in two sections. The first section is made up of practice questions, graduated according to the Attainment Targets and Levels as described by Science in the National Curriculum at Key Stage 2. The tests are arranged to cover in turn the Areas of Study from the three Attainment Targets – Life Processes and Living Things, Materials and Their Properties and Physical Processes. Elements of Attainment Target 1, Experimental and Investigative Science, for example the idea of fair testing and using data, are incorporated into these questions where appropriate.

The second section contains three practice tests similar to those likely to be encountered in the official National Curriculum tests given at the end of Key Stage 2. Although each test does not cover all the Areas of Study from the entire Programme of Study, the combination of questions in all three tests do.

Using this book

The two sections of the book may be used in different ways but the more obvious will be as follows:

1. After a section of work based on areas from the Programme of Study for Key Stage 2, making use of the practice questions to identify what pupils know and understand. This can take place during all four years in that key stage.
2. After a section of work, or at the end of a year, selecting appropriate practice questions to form a test paper in order to help assess pupils' progression.
3. Setting the practice tests during Year 6 and basing revision upon the results.
4. In Year 6, using the practice questions as the basis for revision.

The Key Stage 2 practice questions

The practice questions are highly focused so as to cover each of the Areas of Study from the Programme of Study for Key Stage 2. Each page, or sequence of pages, covers a particular Area of Study at a level commensurate with the degree of difficulty indicated by the published Level Descriptions. Each page could be set as a test in its own right either for individual pupils or the class as a whole. It is recommended that pupils spend about ten minutes on each page of questions. The outcomes will offer teachers some indication of the pupils' strengths and weaknesses so that specific help can be planned.

The Key Stage 2 practice tests

Whilst these practice tests are not intended to look exactly like the actual National Curriculum tests, they are presented on the page in a similar way. There are a wide range of questions written in different styles to prepare pupils for what they might encounter. Pupils are expected to write their answers on a line or within a space, or tick the appropriate boxes, as with the official tests, and there is a margin alongside each page where teachers will put their marks.

Setting the practice tests

Each practice test is 8 pages long and should take pupils about 35 minutes to complete. Each test is graduated so that questions start at Level 3 and move on to Levels 4 and 5. It might be advisable to let pupils start by attempting a section at a time, phasing the whole test over two or three days. In this way, they will be able to give of their best without becoming tired and it may give you a better chance to mark these smaller sections over a longer period.

Similarly, whilst each test is designed to be completed in 35 minutes, for practice you could allow about 30 minutes for each section. Eventually, pupils can be asked to complete the whole test in the correct time.

Carrying out the practice tests and questions

It is recommended that pupils sit as far apart as is practicable when completing the tests. Ask them to carry out the test in silence and to complete it on their own. Tell them to ask you if there are words they cannot read or do not understand. Read these words or phrases to pupils who have difficulty, particularly specific scientific words, e.g. insulator, predator. Some questions will require scientific words in the answers, e.g. evaporated, gravity. The help given should be confined to reading or writing words rather than explaining their meaning. Pupils will need a pencil, a ruler and a rubber to write their answers. It is also advisable for them to have a reading book available in case they finish the test early. They should be instructed to write their answers in the space available on the sheet. The number of lines will usually indicate how much to write. Some answers will require them to tick boxes. Ask the pupils not to write in the margin on each page which contains circles for the teacher's marks. (The maximum number of marks for each question is given below each circle).

Finally, advise the pupils to read the questions carefully and then answer as many questions as they can as they work through the practice test. If they cannot answer a question they should move on and come back to it at the end of the test.

Revising for the tests

It would seem hard to expect pupils to remember all their work in Science during the end of Key Stage 2 tests. The Programme of Study is designed to be studied over four years. It is unrealistic to think that pupils can revise all this work in the few weeks leading up to the tests. It is therefore important to have some planned programme for revision that will enable pupils to show to best advantage what they do know and understand on the day of the test. Revision in Year 6 might take several forms:

*   Throughout the year, pupils are set some of the practice questions for research and completion at home.
*   Practice questions are displayed in the class and pupils are encouraged to take time during the week to answer them.
*   The practice tests and questions are given and the pupils mark their own papers. The discussion about correct answers will provide the revision.
*   Pupils are given time to research a particular topic, e.g. forces, then given appropriate practice questions.

Revision is not confined to Year 6, a similar pattern can be used for younger pupils. For these pupils, revision can be based around selections from the practice questions and tests at appropriate levels of difficulty.

Marking the practice questions and tests

A simple marking scheme is provided for every question with a range of acceptable alternative answers.

Interpreting the results

It is expected by SCAA (the Schools' Curriculum and Assessment Authority) that by the end of Key Stage 2, the majority of pupils will have attained Level 4 as the result of studying the Programme of Study for Science in the National

Curriculum. Some pupils will exceed this national expectation and attain Level 5 and a few exceptional pupils will attain Level 6. Many pupils will be working towards this national expectation and attain Level 3.

During Key Stage 2, pupils in Years 3 and 4 might reasonably be expected to be working within the range of Levels 3 and 4 with some requiring help at Level 2. Older pupils will normally be working within the Level 4/5 range.

The marking sheets for each test give a very clear indication of levelness and therefore how well a pupil is progressing through the Programme of Study for Key Stage 2. More importantly, the marks will tell a teacher exactly where a pupil has succeeded or failed and thus enable extension and remedial work to take place. The marks and levels generated by the practice questions and tests will also provide teachers with the evidence needed to decide whether a pupil should be entered for the Key Stage 2 Tasks at Levels 1 and 2 or the extension paper for Level 6.

Essential assessments marking scheme

It is recognised that teachers would welcome some indication about which level a pupil is at. The following marking scheme is designed to help you find levels at which pupils are operating for the component Attainment Targets as well as for their Science overall. In Science, the levels achieved are broadly described as follows:

- At Level 3 pupils can identify and describe cause and effect relationships, i.e. that happens because of this (e.g. poor diet affects health).
- At Level 4 pupils show simple scientific knowledge (e.g. name the main organs of the body), and use this knowledge to explain cause and effect relationships (e.g. not enough fruit affects health because fruit contains vitamins).
- At Level 5 pupils can show more advanced scientific knowledge (e.g. the heart is used to pump blood around the body), and apply this to show greater understanding (e.g. the more exercise, the faster the heart beats because the muscles need extra sugar which is carried in the blood).

Instructions for marking practice questions

Mark the answers given on the practice questions and put the score in the circles provided in the margins on the right or left of each page. The figure beneath each circle indicates the maximum number of marks available for each part of that question. Total the marks given for each page/section and write it in the total box. To attain Levels 3, 4 or 5 for a particular page or section of questions, pupils should obtain 75 per cent or more of the available marks.

Instructions for marking practice tests

The National Curriculum tests in Science provide teachers with a simple one-figure level for each child. This level represents what the child has achieved over all three Attainment Targets — Life Processes and Living Things (Sc2), Materials and their Properties (Sc3) and Physical Processes (Sc3). These test papers give children the opportunity to demonstrate Levels 3, 4 and 5. In the official test, there is an extension paper which enables children to attain Level 6. This one-figure level does not help to identify the strengths and weaknesses that a child has. The following marking scheme is designed to help you find the overall level as well as that for the individual components.

Instructions

1. Mark the test pages using the marking schemes provided and put the scores in the circles as you mark.
2. Total the number of points for each page and write them in the total box.
3. Transfer the total mark for each page to the grids below.

4. Total the marks to give a score.
5. Use the tables below to find the level for each paper.

TEST 1 – 43 marks available

Child scores:	Probable level attained:
32 marks or more	Level 5
23 marks to 31 marks	Level 4
15 marks to 22 marks	Level 3
14 marks and below	Working towards Level 3

TEST 2 – 51 marks available

Child scores:	Probable level attained:
40 marks or more	Level 5
28 marks to 39 marks	Level 4
18 marks to 27 marks	Level 3
17 marks and below	Working towards Level 3

TEST 3 – 49 marks available

Child scores:	Probable level attained:
40 marks or more	Level 5
27 marks to 39 marks	Level 4
16 marks to 26 marks	Level 3
15 marks and below	Working towards Level 3

TEST 1		TEST 2		TEST 3	
Question	Mark	Question	Mark	Question	Mark
Q1		Q1		Q1	
Q2		Q2		Q2	
Q3		Q3		Q3	
Q4		Q4		Q4	
Q5		Q5		Q5	
Q6		Q6		Q6	
Q7		Q7		Q7	
Q8		Q8		Q8	
Q9					
Total		Total		Total	

Notes for teachers

To find how well children have done for each component

1 On each test page, the circles showing the total marks possible for each question have a code to indicate which Attainment Target is being tested. These codes are Sc2, Sc3 and Sc4.

2 To find out how well the child is doing in each Attainment Target, add up the scores for Sc2, Sc3 and Sc4 and consult the tables below for probable levels.

TEST 1	Sc2 Life Processes and Living Things	Sc3 Materials and their Properties	Sc4 Physical Processes
Level 5	13 and above	8 and above	11 and above
Level 4	9 to 12	6 and 7	8 to 10
Level 3	6 to 8	4 and 5	5 to 7
Working towards Level 3	1 to 5	1 to 3	1 to 4

TEST 2	Sc2 Life Processes and Living Things	Sc3 Materials and their Properties	Sc4 Physical Processes
Level 5	17 and above	15 and above	8 and above
Level 4	12 to 16	11 to 14	6 and 7
Level 3	8 to 11	7 to 10	4 and 5
Working towards Level 3	7 and below	6 and below	3 and below

TEST 3	Sc2 Life Processes and Living Things	Sc3 Materials and their Properties	Sc4 Physical Processes
Level 5	14	12	14
Level 4	10 to 13	8 to 11	9 to 13
Level 3	6 to 9	5 to 7	5 to 8
Working towards Level 3	5 or below	4 or below	4 or below

Life Processes and Living Things

LIFE PROCESSES

1 Have a look at this cat sitting next to a plant. In front of the cat is a clockwork plastic mouse.

a. Tick **one** box which is by the word that shows one thing that the cat and the plastic mouse can both do:

Reproduce ☐

Move ☐

Grow ☐

Breathe ☐

1

b. How do you know that the cat and plant must both be living things?

Tick **two** boxes

They reproduce ☐

They eat food ☐

They make food ☐

They grow ☐

2

TOTAL

○
2

c. What must the plant do to stay alive?

Tick **two** boxes

Take in water ☐

Eat food ☐

Move ☐

Stay in sunlight ☐

2 Class 4 were carrying out experiments to find out more about living things.

Samantha took some sugar crystals, tied them with cotton, found out how heavy they were and then put them into a very strong sugar solution. After a week, she found that the crystals had grown and were heavier.

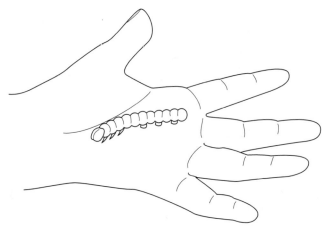

Jason kept a caterpillar. He measured how heavy it was. Every day for a week, he fed it leaves and gave it some water. At the end of the week the caterpillar was longer and heavier.

Sarah looked after some cress plants for a week. At the start she measured how long the seedlings were. After watering them every day, at the end of the week, she found the seedlings were longer.

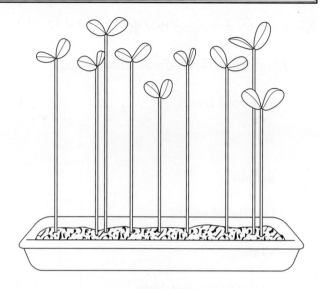

a. Tick **two** of the following words which say what the sugar crystal, caterpillar and cress seedling have in common?

They are all living ☐

They all grow in size ☐

They all need food ☐

They are all eaten ☐

2

b. Tick **two** boxes that show that the caterpillar is an animal:

Makes its own food ☐

Moves from place to place ☐

Reproduces ☐

Eats food ☐

Needs to live in the light ☐

2

c. Write what a cress seedling can do because it is a plant.

_____

1

TOTAL

Life Processes

1 Animals are living things.

What **four** things do all animals do?

Tick **four** boxes

Fly	☐	Swim	☐
Breathe	☐	Lay eggs	☐
Get rid of waste	☐	Make a noise	☐
Walk	☐	Move	☐
Make their own food	☐	Feed	☐
Hear	☐	Make nests	☐

○
4

2 All plants are living things.

What **three** things are true about all plants?

Tick **three** boxes

They reproduce ☐

They make their own food ☐

They use ready-made food ☐

They produce flowers ☐

They grow ☐

They grow from bulbs ☐

○
3

TOTAL

◯
2

3 If you were shipwrecked and had to live on a desert island, what would be the most important things you would need to do to stay alive?

Tick **two** boxes

Make a shelter ☐

Drink water ☐

Make your bed every day ☐

Keep warm ☐

Eat food ☐

Have a wash every day ☐

Read books ☐

Exercise every day ☐

8

10

1 This table shows how animals and plants are living. It also shows the differences between them.

Write in the missing words.

Feature	Meaning	Animals	Plants
Respire	Use oxygen to get energy from food	Yes	_____
_____	Get rid of waste	Yes	Yes
Nutrition	Make their food	_____	Yes
Movement		Yes	No
_____	Use food to get bigger	Yes	Yes
Are sensitive	React quickly	Yes	_____
Reproduction	Produce young	_____	_____

2 Look at the pictures. From what you know about living things, write L if you think it is a living thing, N if it is non-living and D if you think it is dead.

Salt crystal

Wood

Plastic ruler

Cotton thread

Cork

Worm

Stone

Water

Acorn

Sponge

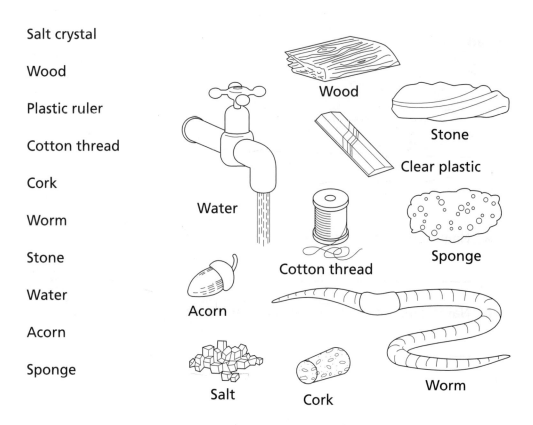

Life Processes and Living Things

HUMANS AS ORGANISMS

1 Justin cleans his teeth every morning when he wakes just before he eats his breakfast. Simon always cleans his teeth after breakfast and just before he goes to bed. Susan cleans her teeth when she remembers to.
All three went to the dentist .

Can you explain why:

    a. Susan needed to have three teeth filled?

    _____

    b. Simon had no fillings and Justin needed one?

    _____

2 On this plate there are different types of food.

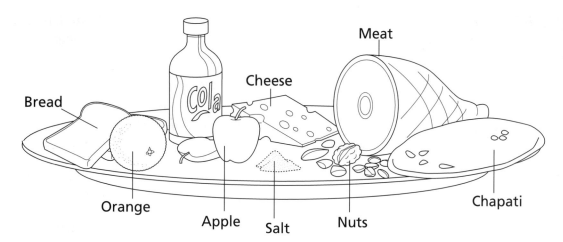

    a. Name **two** foods which will help you grow.

    _____

    b. Name **two** foods which help you get the energy to run around.

    _____

1

1

2

2

TOTAL

2

2

1

c. Name **two** foods which keep you healthy.

_____

d. Name **two** foods which could give you tooth decay.

_____

3   a. On this picture, mark with an H where you could listen and hear the heartbeat.

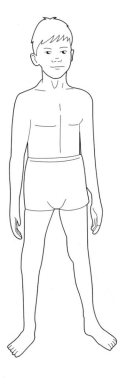

It is easier to use a stethoscope to hear the heart beat. Alison listened to her partner's heartbeat and counted 72 beats every minute. Her partner then stepped on and off a chair for 1 minute and Alison counted again.

1

b. Which of these heartbeats do you think Alison heard?

Put a tick in **one** box

62 heartbeats every minute ☐

72 heartbeats every minute ☐

75 heartbeats every minute ☐

100 heartbeats every minute ☐

4 When you move your arms and legs, the muscles that move them get thicker.

    a. On these drawings, draw **one** arrow where you think the muscle will get thicker.

Raising your arm

Raising your foot

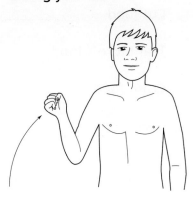

2

1

5   **b.** What does the muscle pull against inside both the arm and the leg?

_____

On the side of a packet of aspirins is written:

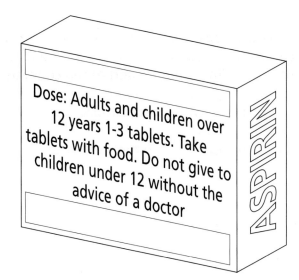

Dose: Adults and children over 12 years 1-3 tablets. Take tablets with food. Do not give to children under 12 without the advice of a doctor

ASPIRIN

1

Why is this warning given on packets of aspirin?

_____

Humans as Organisms

1 There are four different kinds of teeth in our mouths: premolars, molars, incisors and canines. Each does a special job.

    a. Match the different teeth with the jobs they do. The first one is done for you.

Premolars	Cut food
Molars	Tear bits off food
Incisors	Crush food
Canines	Grind food

    b. Which **three** of these things should you do to keep your teeth healthy?

    Tick **three** boxes

brush your teeth before meals ☐

chew gum ☐

brush your teeth after meals ☐

eat sugary foods ☐

drink milk ☐

visit the dentist regularly ☐

2 On this drawing of the human body there are four parts labelled A, B, C and D. Write down which of the following body organs they represent.

heart   **lungs**   **small intestine**   **kidney**

Part A _____

Part B _____

Part C _____

Part D _____

3

3

4

TOTAL

16

3 After we eat food through our mouth, it passes through the organs of the digestive system and the bits we do not use leave through the anus.

Put the organs listed below in the order that food passes through them.

large intestine　　　　**small intestine**　　　　**stomach**

First　　　___in through the mouth___

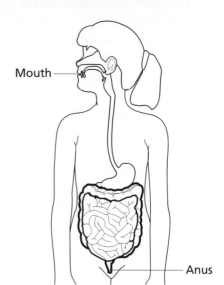

Second　　_____

Third　　　_____

Fourth　　 _____

Last　　　　___out through the anus___

○
3

4 The heart is found in the chest and acts as a pump.

   a. What is moved round the body when the heart pumps?

   _____

   b. What **two** kinds of blood vessels carry dissolved food, oxygen and other things round the body?

   _____

You can tell how fast your heart beats by feeling the pulse on your wrist. Here is Sean's pulse rate at different times:

○
1

○
2

What Sean is doing	The number of pulses felt in 1 minute
Sitting	75
Walking	100
Jogging	140
Running	190

   c. How does exercise affect the way Sean's heart beats?

   _____

○
1

TOTAL

Humans as Organisms

5 These sentences describe stages of the life cycle of humans. Use the following words to complete the sentences:

child   puberty   foetus   milk   adults   baby   egg

Use each word **only once**:

After children reach _____ they mature, grow and become

_____ .

When a sperm fertilises an _____ in the womb a _____ is produced.

When it is very young a _____ feeds on _____ .

A baby eats solid food and grows into a _____ .

1 Fluoride is a mineral found in water. In some places the amount of fluoride is high, in other places it is low. Dentists looked at children from two places with different amounts of fluoride in the water. They looked at 100 children from each place to see how many fillings they had.

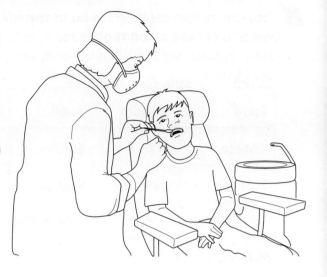

Number of fillings	Number of children with this number of fillings	
	High fluoride area	Low fluoride area
None	61	21
1 to 5	32	43
6 to 10	5	22
11 to 15	2	10
16 to 20	0	4

a. What do the results tell you about the link between tooth decay and the amount of fluoride in the water?

_____

1

b. Write down **three** things the children in these low fluoride areas could do to help to reduce tooth decay.

1. _____

2. _____

3. _____

3

TOTAL

2 Calcium in the diet helps to build strong teeth and bones. Look at this table which gives the amount of calcium (milligrams) found in different kinds of food. Figures are for 100 g of food, except for milk (1 pint), cola (1 glass) and tea (1 cup).

Food	Calcium	Food	Calcium	Food	Calcium
Cheese	800	Sardines	550	Sausages	55
Pint of milk	729	Pilchards	300	Bacon	13
Glass of cola	4	Cup of tea	1	Tomatoes	13
Butter	15	Tuna	15	Lamb chop	9
Chapatis	66	Greens	86	Chips	14
Bread (two slices)	100	Baked beans	45	Apple	3
Cornflakes	4	Potatoes	4	Pear	6
Milk chocolate	220	Peanuts	61	Banana	4

a. Write down **three** foods that you should eat if you want to have healthy teeth and bones.

_____

○ 3

b. Which lunch would give you the most calcium?

Show your working in the answer you give.

_____

○ 1

1

2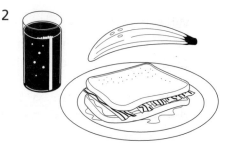

Menu A:

2 lamb chops (200 g)
chips (100 g), baked beans (100 g)
a chapati (50 g) and a pear (100g)

Menu B:

a bacon sandwich (100 g)
with buttered bread (2 slices)
a banana (100 g) and a glass of cola.

3 **a.** On this drawing of the outside of the heart, can you match the following words with the labels 1, 2, 3 and 4?

Ventricle **(Write V)**

Auricle **(Write A)**

Main artery taking
blood to body **(Write M)**

Vein returning
blood from lungs **(Write L)**

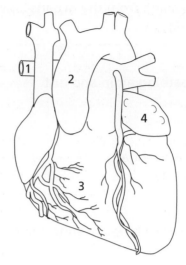

○
4

This graph shows a girl's heartbeat during playtime.

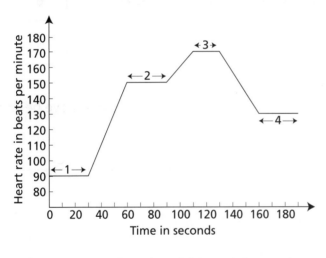

At 1 the girl was sitting on the ground.

At 2 she was running slowly.

At 3 she was skipping.

b. Suggest what the girl was doing at 4.

_____

○
1

c. What was the rate of the girl's heartbeat while she was skipping?

_____

○
1

d. How long did it take for the rate of the girl's heartbeat to change from the slow running rate to the skipping rate?

_____

○
1

TOTAL

4 The main organs in the human body do special jobs.

Draw a line from the organs labelled A, B, C and D in the drawing to the jobs they do:

Breathing air in and out

Storing sugar

Pumping blood around the body

Digestion of food

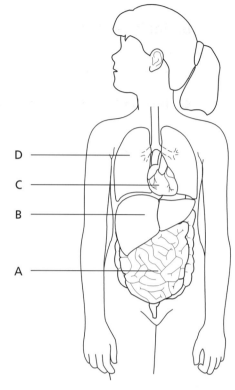

5

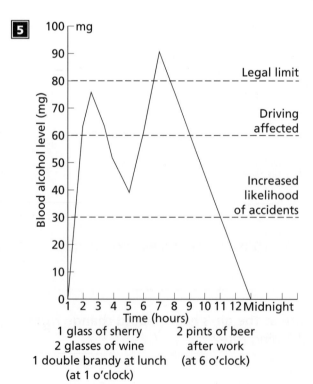

Blood alcohol level (mg)

Legal limit

Driving affected

Increased likelihood of accidents

Time (hours)

1 glass of sherry   2 pints of beer
2 glasses of wine   after work
1 double brandy at lunch (at 6 o'clock)
   (at 1 o'clock)

When a person drinks alcohol it finds its way into the bloodstream.

This graph shows the change in blood alcohol levels of an adult male who drinks a glass of sherry, two glasses of wine and a double brandy with his lunch and later, after work, drinks two pints of beer. He then drives home.

THE FACTS
When there is 30 mg of alcohol or more in the blood the chances of having a driving accident are higher.

It is against the law to drive with over 80 mg of alcohol in the blood.

TOTAL

a. For how long is the level of alcohol in this man's blood likely to affect his driving and possibly cause an accident?

_____

1

b. For how long is the man over the legal limit?

_____

1

c. Is it safe for him to drive to work the next morning?

_____

1

TOTAL

Life Processes and Living Things

GREEN PLANTS AS ORGANISMS

1 Class 5 were trying to find out the best way to grow plants. They grew half of a packet of cress seeds in one dish and the other half in a second dish. In both dishes they sowed the seeds on cotton wool. They added the same amount of water to each dish every day. The teacher put one dish in a dark cupboard and left the other on a ledge under a sunny window.

After a week, the two dishes looked like this but the teacher could not remember where each had been grown:

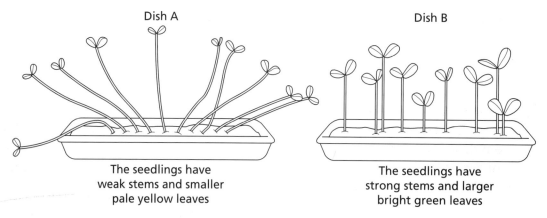

Dish A

Dish B

The seedlings have weak stems and smaller pale yellow leaves

The seedlings have strong stems and larger bright green leaves

Where had he kept dish A?

_____

Where had he kept dish B?

_____

2 Class 5 carefully pulled up two plants of the common weed groundsel from the school garden and put them in two pots. They watered one pot but not the other. Here is what the two plants looked like after 2 days.

Which of the groundsel plants was given water?

_____

TOTAL

3 A piece of celery was left for a few hours in a jar of water which was coloured red with food dye.

What would the leaf veins look like after two hours?

_____

◯

1

4 Suni and Katie were testing how fast different seeds would fall. They took sycamore, maple, hornbeam and ash seeds. These seeds have wings which slow them down when they fall.
Suni dropped them from the top of a ladder and Katie timed how long it took them to hit the ground and marked the spot where each seed landed.

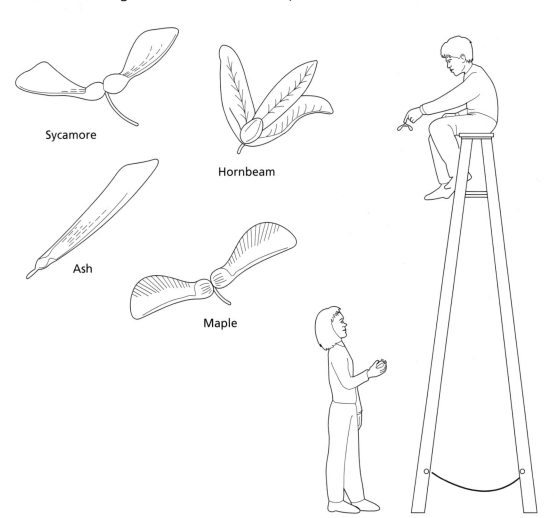

Sycamore

Hornbeam

Ash

Maple

Here are the results:

Seed	How long it took to fall
Ash	2.5 seconds
Sycamore	5 seconds
Hornbeam	3.5 seconds
Maple	4.5 seconds

a. Which seed took the longest to fall?

_____

b. Which seed do you think landed closest to the ladder?

_____

c. Which seed do you think landed furthest away from the ladder?

_____

Why do you think that?

_____

1

1

1

1

TOTAL

1 Class 6 carried out experiments to find out about roots. They planted five beans in soil and watered them every day. They made a small hole in each bean and tied a piece of raffia through the hole to make a loop in order to find out how much force was needed to pull the bean seedlings from the soil as they grew. They measured this force for a different bean every three days using a Newton-meter. Here are the results:

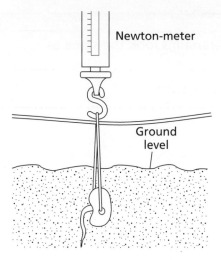

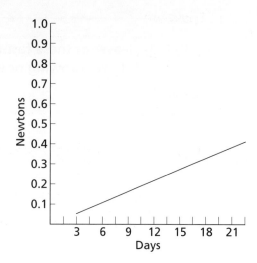

a. As the bean grew, was it easier or harder to pull it from the soil?

_____

○
1

b. How does the way that the roots grow help the bean plant?

_____

○
1

c. What other jobs do the roots do for the bean seedling?

_____

○
1

2 A grower sells geranium plants all the year round.
He grows some in a heated greenhouse;
some in a barn that is kept warm and dark
and others in a barn that is kept quite cold.
All the geranium plants are watered every day.

TOTAL

a. Which geraniums will take the longest to grow?

_____

◯ 1

b. Which geraniums will grow the most quickly?

_____

◯ 1

c. Will the leaves of these fast-growing geraniums look the same as those of slower growing ones?

_____

◯ 1

3 **a.** Here is a drawing of a crocus flower. What are the names of the parts labelled A, B, C and D.

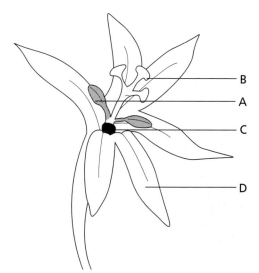

Part A _____

Part B _____

Part C _____

◯ 4

Part D _____

b. Show the correct order of the stages in the life of a flowering plant by linking the order in Column 1 with the stages shown in Column 2. The first one has been done for you.

◯ 5

Column 1	Column 2
Order	Stages
First ———————	Seed formed
Second	Flower forms
Third	New plant grows
Fourth	Flower is pollinated
Fifth	Seed germinates
Sixth	Seed disperses

TOTAL

4 Jessica and Claire were working in the school garden to find out which insects visited different flowers. They counted how many times different insects visited each type of flower. Here is their record:

Insect / Flower	Flies	Beetles	Bees	Butterflies	Wasps	Ants
Buttercup	5	3	1	0	1	4
Clover	0	0	8	3	0	0
Hogweed	5	4	0	0	3	2
Nettle	0	0	7	8	0	0
Rockrose	3	4	0	0	1	2
Vetch	0	0	4	0	0	0

a. Which plant had the greatest variety of visitors?

_____

b. Which **three** plants do bees prefer?

_____

c. Why do insects visit the flowers?

_____

d. How do insects help the flowers they visit?

_____

1

3

1

2

TOTAL

1 Which **three** factors can affect the way that plants grow?

1. _____   2. _____   3. _____

2 Plants produce their own food. This can be stored as starch. Iodine solution changes starch to a deep blue colour.

Some children were trying to find out how plants make their food. They took a geranium plant, covered four of the leaves with some aluminium foil and left the other four uncovered. The plant was left on a window ledge and watered every day. After four days, the two sets of leaves were removed and tested to see if there was any starch present.

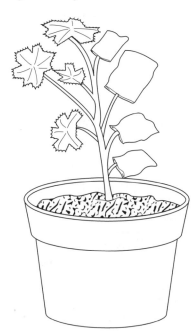

    a. What do you think the results were? Complete these sentences.

       1. The leaves without foil _____

       2. The leaves with the foil _____

    b. Why do you think this?

    _____

3

1

1

3

3 Here is a drawing of a young bean plant.

a. Plants can make their own food. Which part of the plant usually does this?

_____

b. Give **two** jobs done by the root hairs.

1. _____

_____

2. _____

_____

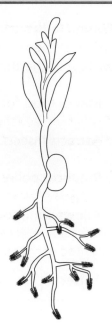

As the plant gets older, the roots grow downwards and sideways.

c. Why do the roots grow sideways?

_____

4 This picture shows a strawberry plant. Four organs are labelled A, B, C and D.

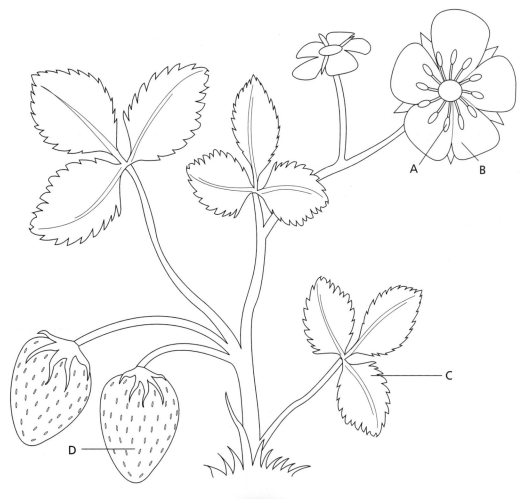

1

2

2

1

TOTAL

31

Complete the table below by writing the names of the organs in the second column. Then choose the correct job for each organ from the list given and write it in the third column.

Makes food for the plant

Attracts birds for pollination

Attracts insects for pollination

Attracts animals for seed dispersal

Produces pollen

Protects the plant from animals

Allows wind to carry seeds

Letter	Name of organ	Job it does
A		
B		
C		
D		

8

TOTAL

Life Processes and Living Things

VARIATION AND CLASSIFICATION

1 These drawings are of birds found on the mud by the seashore.

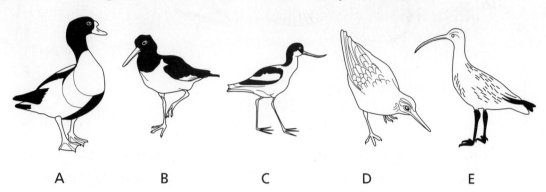

A   B   C   D   E

Use the information in this table to find the names of the five birds.

	Snipe	Curlew	Oyster catcher	Shellduck	Avocet
Shape of feet	not webbed	not webbed	not webbed	webbed	not webbed
Shape of beak	straight, long	bent downwards	straight, short	short	bent upwards
Length of leg	short	long	short	short	long

The name of bird A is   _____

The name of bird B is   _____

The name of bird C is   _____

The name of bird D is   _____

The name of bird E is   _____

5

TOTAL

Variation and Classification

1 Here are drawings of some animals called shellfish that are found on the seashore. You can use this key to find out their names.

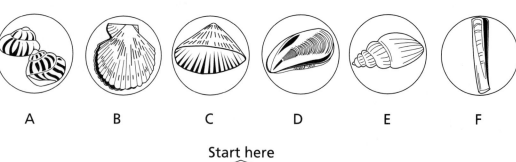

A   B   C   D   E   F

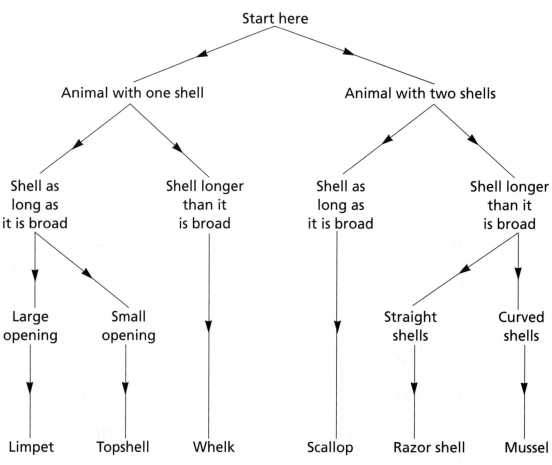

The name of shell A is _____

The name of shell B is _____

The name of shell C is _____

The name of shell D is _____

The name of shell E is _____

The name of shell F is _____

6

Variation and Classification

1 Use the key to find the names of these twigs which come from common woodland trees. The twigs are shown the way they look in winter.

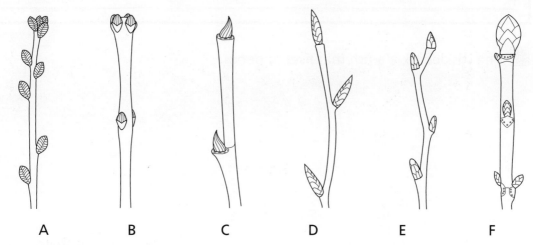

A   B   C   D   E   F

1. Buds grow in opposite pairs on the twig . . . . Go to 2

   Buds do not grow in opposite pairs . . . . Go to 3

2. Buds longer than they are wide . . . . Horse chestnut

   Buds as long as they are wide . . . . Ash

3. Buds much longer than they are wide . . . . Beech

   Buds not very long and thin . . . . Go to 4

4. Buds have stripes . . . . Plane

   Buds not striped . . . . Go to 5

5. Buds in a group at end of twig . . . . Oak

   Buds not in group at end of twig . . . . Elm

The name of twig A is _____

The name of twig B is _____

The name of twig C is _____

The name of twig D is _____

The name of twig E is _____

The name of twig F is _____

6

TOTAL

Life Processes and Living Things

LIVING THINGS IN THEIR ENVIRONMENT

1 The stickleback is a fish that lives in ponds.

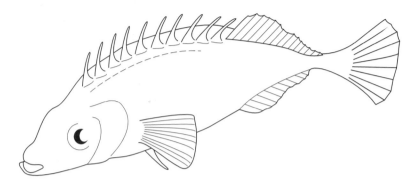

a. Write the names of **three** parts of the body of the stickleback that help it to live in water. Say **how** each part helps.

Part   Helps it to

1. _____   _____

2. _____   _____

3. _____   _____

b. How does the shape of the stickleback help it to move?

_____

2

2

2

1

TOTAL

36

2   **a.**   Here is a list of animals and plants. Draw arrows to link these names to the sort of habitat in which you would expect to find each of these animals and plants:

Starfish

Owl

Mussel

Worm

Newt

Seaweed

Bluebell

Crab

Woodlouse

Frog

Pondweed

Snail

Water snail

Woodpecker

Centipede

Butterfly

 Pond

 Soil

 Sea

 Air

16

   b.   Look at the group of animals that you find in the air. What have they all got in common that helps them to fly?

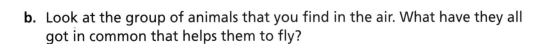

1

TOTAL

3 Some animals eat other animals, some eat plants and some can eat both animals and plants. Look at the teeth of the animals below.
The **incisors** are as sharp as scissors and can be used for cutting food such as leaves.
The **canines** are pointed and can be used for tearing flesh (meat).
At the back of the mouth, there are teeth called **molars** which can grind food like seeds into small pieces.

These three drawings show the skulls and teeth of animals A, B and C.

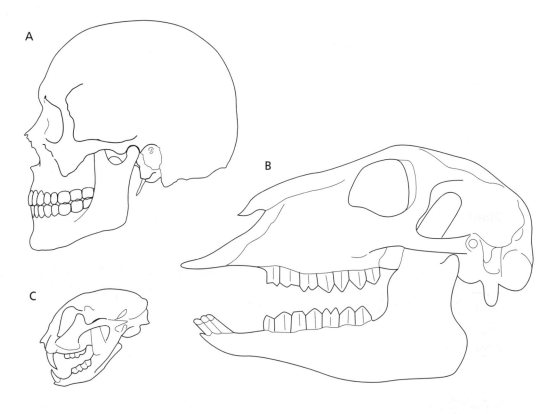

a. Which animal mainly eats plants?

_____

b. How can you tell which of the animals eats the flesh of other animals?

_____

1

1

Living Things in their Environment

1 Here are five food chains found on the seashore.

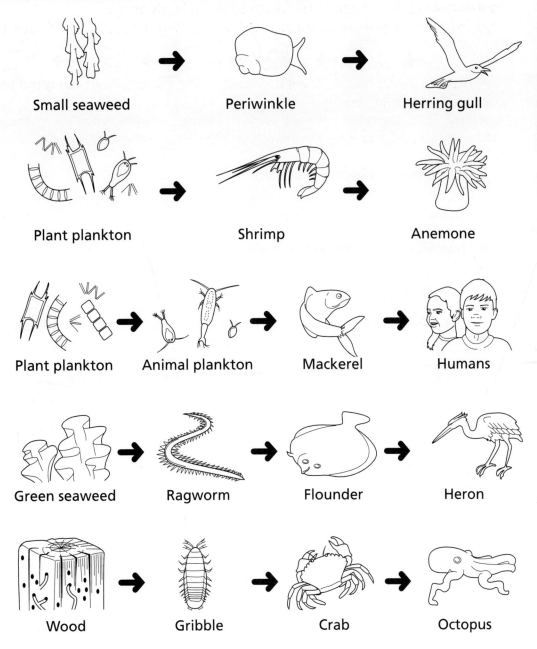

In the table below write the names of **three** producers, **three** first consumers and **three** second consumers from these food chains.

Producers	First consumers	Second consumers

9

2 Here is one food chain involving some animals and plants that live in a woodland.

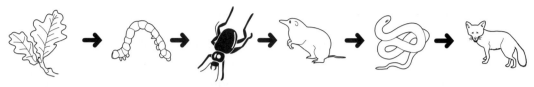

Oak leaves   Caterpillar   Hunting beetle   Shrew   Grass snake   Fox

a. Name the producer in the chain.

_____

b. Name two predators in the chain.

_____

c. Tick **three** boxes to show three things all the consumers in the food chain must do to stay alive:

Eat food ☐

Lay eggs ☐

Breathe ☐

Keep clean ☐

Get rid of waste materials ☐

Live in holes ☐

1 ◯

2 ◯

3 ◯

3 Barn owls prey mainly on small mammals and birds. You can tell what an owl has eaten because, every day or so, it sicks up pellets of the bones, fur and feathers it cannot digest. The graph shows what was found in some owl pellets collected over about a week:

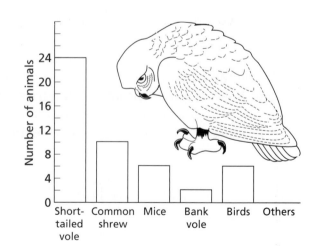

a. What is the most common food of barn owls?

_____

1

b. Name **three** ways the barn owl is suited to catch its prey.

1. _____

1

2. _____

1

3. _____

1

1 Class 6 were investigating the factors that affect where grass grows around the school grounds. When the class compared their findings, Josh found that there was very little under most of the trees.
Ruth said there was a lot of grass between the trees.
Andrew noted that whilst there was a lot of grass on the football pitch, he found very little in the goalmouth.
Amy found that in the nature area, which is surrounded by a wire fence, the grass grows very long.
Richard said he found rabbit droppings everywhere except in the nature area.

Explain what might be affecting the growth of grass:

1. Under the tree

_____

2. In the goalmouth

_____

3. In the nature area

_____

1

1

1

TOTAL

2 Lichens are small living things that are often found growing on the bark of tree trunks, rocks and roofs. There are three types of lichen: flat lichen, leafy lichen and shrubby lichen. Some lichens are sensitive to air pollution and for this reason their presence, or absence, can tell you about the level of pollution in a place.

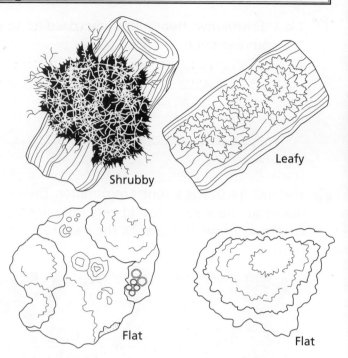

Here are the results of a survey of air pollution in an area of a town with quite a few chemical factories. The different types of lichen were counted in the town centre and then at fixed distances on the way out of town.

Distance from town centre	Number of flat lichens found	Number of leafy lichens found	Number of shrubby lichens found
0	1	0	0
1 kilometre (km)	1	0	0
2 km	2	0	0
4 km	8	0	0
6 km	15	2	0
8 km	20	8	1
10 km	20	16	10

a. Which type of lichen is most resistant to air pollution?

_____

1

b. How far from the town centre can you find all three lichens?

_____

1

TOTAL

c. Write down **two** things you could do to make sure that the tests carried out are fair?

_____

_____

3 This picture shows a forest in summer. The oak trees make large canopies of branches and leaves that let very little light get through to the forest floor. Foxgloves grow underneath the oak trees. They produce blue and purple flowers.

a. Write down **two** reasons why the foxglove is suited to its environment.

1. _____

2. _____

Some typical food chains in the forest are as follows:

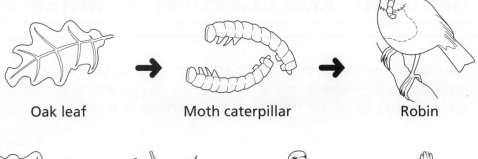

Oak leaf   Moth caterpillar   Robin

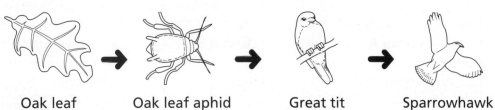

Oak leaf   Oak leaf aphid   Great tit   Sparrowhawk

b. Write down **two** ways in which the second consumers are suited to their environment.

1. _____

2. _____

Micro-organisms can be found in the leaf litter and soil on the floor of the forest.

c. What important job do these micro-organisms do?

_____

d. Give one way in which micro-organisms can be harmful to humans.

_____

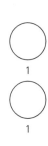

1

1

1

1

TOTAL

Materials and their Properties

GROUPING AND CLASSIFYING MATERIALS

1 The class visited a large department store. As they walked round, the children wrote down the names of some of the goods on sale and what they were made of. They sorted the goods into three groups A, B and C.

Group A	Group B	Group C
Aluminium foil	Oak box	Polythene bag
Brass screw	Ash table	Polystyrene cup
Iron nail	Pine cupboard	PVC coat
Copper bracelet	Walnut wardrobe	Acrylic jumper
Gold ring	Beech chair	Nylon carpet

What is the reason for them putting these things into the three groups?

Group A _____

Group B _____

Group C _____

1

1

1

2 Here is some information about different kinds of plastic. The first column of boxes tells you what they are like, the second column says what they can be used for.

Draw a line from each plastic to a box which you think shows the best use for that plastic.

Plastic		Best used for

1

It is hard, transparent and does not crack easily

a

Cushions for armchairs

2

Can be made into squashy foam that can be cut to any shape

b

Cloth covers for car seats

3

Can be made into thin bendy fibres which can be woven

c

Windows for telephone boxes

○ 3

TOTAL

3 Here is a drawing of an electrical circuit.

Part A
The outside of
the bulb is hard
and transparent

Part B
The case of the
bulb holder is white
and hard

Part D
The crocodile clips
are hard and a
shiny silver colour

Part C
The covering of
the connector is red
and flexible

4.5 V

Part E
The terminals of the battery
are a shiny gold colour

a. Which two parts are made of metal?

Tick **two** boxes

A ☐   B ☐   C ☐   D ☐   E ☐

b. Which **three** parts will not conduct electricity?

A ☐   B ☐   C ☐   D ☐   E ☐

c. The outside of the bulb is hard. What material is it made of?

Tick **one** box

Metal ☐   Plastic ☐   Glass ☐

d. Tick the property you think is useful for the bulb cover to have.

Tick **one** box

Transparent ☐   Translucent ☐   Opaque ☐

2

3

1

1

TOTAL

4 Link each material to a use and to what makes it good for that use. Use each property only once. Nylon has been done for you.

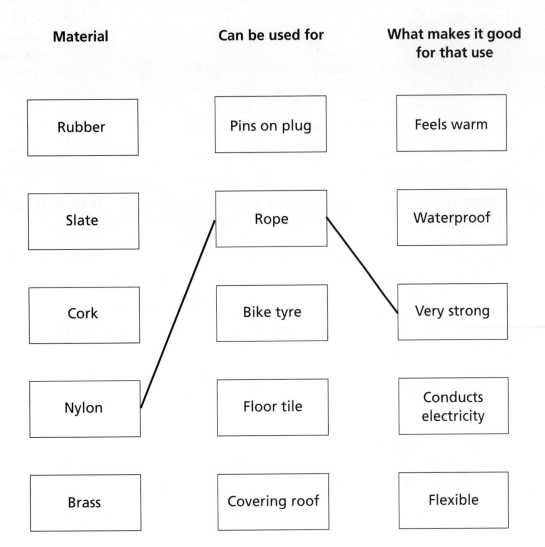

Material	Can be used for	What makes it good for that use
Rubber	Pins on plug	Feels warm
Slate	Rope	Waterproof
Cork	Bike tyre	Very strong
Nylon	Floor tile	Conducts electricity
Brass	Covering roof	Flexible

4

TOTAL

5 The makers of a cold drink machine wanted to use cups that would keep the drinks cold for as long as possible. Here are the results of their experiments.

Type of plastic cup	Temperature of drink at start	Temperature of drink after 10 minutes	Temperature of drink after 20 minutes
Thin polystyrene	10°c	16°c	20°c
Foam polystyrene	10°c	12°c	14°c
Paper	10°c	13°c	16°c
Polycarbonate	10°c	16°c	19°c

a. Which cup should they choose for their machine?

_____

b. How could they make sure the test was fair?

_____

1

1

TOTAL

50

6 You can find out how hard a rock is by trying to scratch it. Here are some results where a number of rocks were scratched using a fingernail, a metal nail and a nail file.

Rock	It could be scratched with a finger nail	It could be scratched with metal nail	It could be scratched with nail file
Chalk	Yes	Yes	Yes
Fluorspar	No	Yes	Yes
Diamond	No	No	No
Calcite crystal	No	Yes	Yes
Quartz rock	No	No	Yes

a. Which rock is the hardest?

_____

1

b. Which rock is the softest?

_____

1

1 A scientist called Friedrich Mohs found a way to measure the hardness of mineral rocks. He took 10 rocks and graded them from 1 for very soft up to 10 for very hard. The place of each rock on the scale depends on how well that rock will scratch other rocks. Each rock can be scratched by the rocks below it in the table.

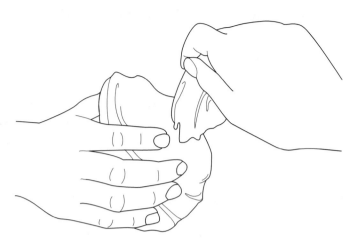

Here is the scale:

Hardness	Rock	
1	Talc	Softest rock
2	Gypsum	
3	Calcite	
4	Fluorspar	
5	Apatite	
6	Felspar	
7	Quartz	
8	Topaz	
9	Corundum	
10	Diamond	Hardest rock

a. Which rocks on the scale will fluorspar scratch?

_____

3

1

1

b. Which rocks will quartz not scratch?

_____

c. If you wanted to find the hardness of an unknown rock and you found that you could scratch it with fluorspar, what test would you try next?

_____

12

2 All materials can be solid, liquid or gas.

a. Write the names of these materials in their correct column:

petrol	oil	paper	ice
air	butter	steam	carbon dioxide
cola	syrup	glass	sugar

Solid	Liquid	Gas

TOTAL

○
5

Solids, liquids and gases can be recognised because they have different properties. The chart below has sentences that describe these properties.

b. Complete the chart by putting a tick in the box by the sentence that you think is true for a solid, liquid or gas.

Some sentences are true for more than one thing. The first one has been done for you.

Property	Solid	Liquid	Gas
Can flow through a tube or pipe		✔	✔
Keeps its own shape			
Is usually rigid or stiff			
Can be squashed into a small space			
Fills the shape of the container			

3 Here are some drawings of common things found in the kitchen of many homes. Each object is made of a material which helps it do its particular job.

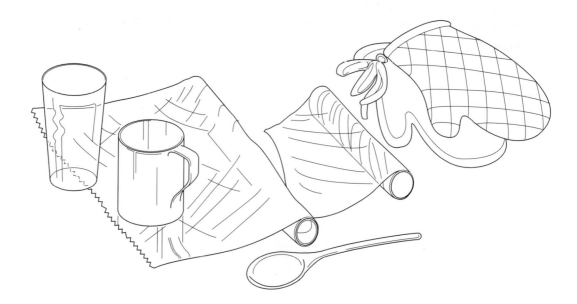

TOTAL

a. Put a tick in the box under those properties that you think enable the objects to do their particular jobs. The first one is done for you.

	Does not conduct heat	See-through	Hard	Easy to bend	Waterproof
Drinking glass		✔	✔		✔
Plastic mug					
Plastic clingfilm					
Wooden spoon					
Aluminium foil					
Oven gloves					

14

4 An alloy is made when a pure metal is mixed with other metals or chemicals. Alloys are made because they are better in some way than the pure metal. The first two columns in the table on page 56 show alloys and the mixtures which are used to make them.
The third column shows some reasons for using the alloy rather than the metal.

Draw a line to link the alloy with the correct reasons for using them.
Pewter is done for you.

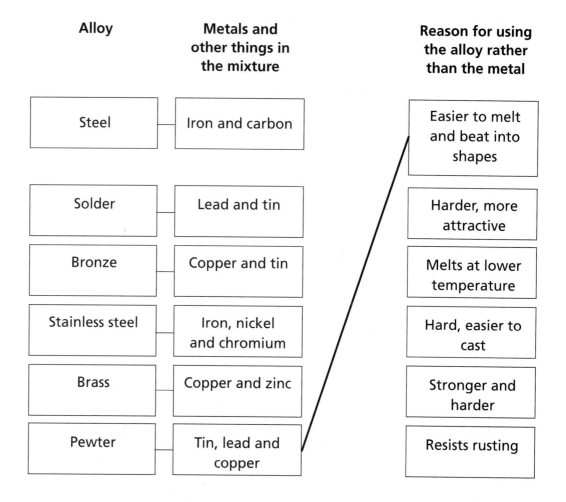

Alloy	Metals and other things in the mixture	Reason for using the alloy rather than the metal
Steel	Iron and carbon	Easier to melt and beat into shapes
Solder	Lead and tin	Harder, more attractive
Bronze	Copper and tin	Melts at lower temperature
Stainless steel	Iron, nickel and chromium	Hard, easier to cast
Brass	Copper and zinc	Stronger and harder
Pewter	Tin, lead and copper	Resists rusting

5 An experiment was carried out to find which tea cosy kept a teapot hottest the longest.

Three tea cosies were chosen: cosy **A** made of knitted wool, cosy **B** made from cloth padded with cotton wool, and cosy **C** made with cloth stuffed with foam plastic.

A teapot was filled with boiling water and the temperature measured in degrees Celsius. After ½ hour, the cosy was removed and the temperature measured again. One experiment without a tea cosy was also carried out.

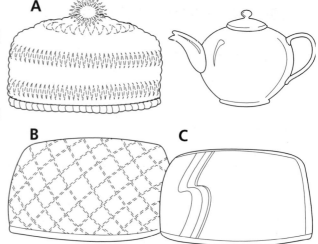

The results were:

Cosy	Temperature at start	Temperature after ½ hour
A Wool	97°C	70°C
B Cloth and cotton wool	98°C	74°C
C Cloth and foam plastic	97°C	56°C
Teapot without cosy	99°C	30°C

a. Which tea cosy, A, B or C, is best at keeping tea hot?

_____

1

b. Why have you chosen this answer?

_____

1

c. Write **one** of the following words to complete the sentence:

        conductor   insulator   capacitor

The best tea cosy is the best _____ .

1

d. Suggest **three** ways to make this experiment a fair test:

1._____

1

2._____

1

3._____

1

6 A factory that made different rulers wanted to find out which type of ruler was the most flexible (bendy).

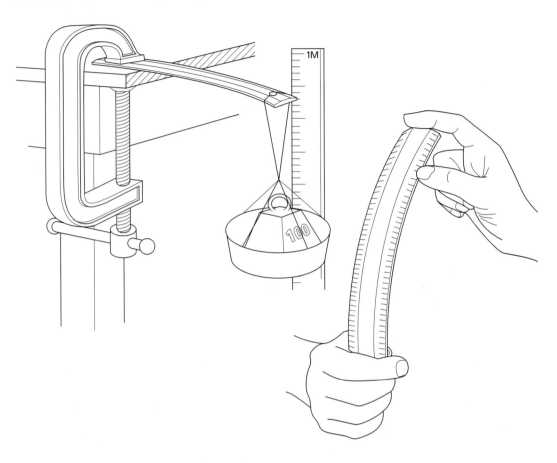

Rulers made of wood, nylon, steel and clear polystyrene were clamped to a table and a pot was hung on the other end. Masses were added gradually to the pot and the amount of bend measured in millimetres (mm) using a rule.

Here are the results:

The amount each ruler bent when the following masses were added.					
Type of ruler	100 g	100 g	300 g	400 g	500 g
Wood	3 mm	5 mm	7 mm	9 mm	11 mm
Nylon	5 mm	9 mm	13 mm	18 mm	23 mm
Steel	4 mm	7 mm	10 mm	13 mm	12 mm
Polystyrene	4 mm	6 mm	8 mm	10 mm	12 mm

a. Which ruler is the bendiest?

_____

1

TOTAL

b. Suggest **three** ways to make this experiment a fair test:

1._____

_____

2._____

_____

3._____

_____

c. If you wanted to use a ruler as a catapult, which type would be the best and why?

I would use the _____ because_____

_____

Grouping and Classifying Materials

1 Nails

Scientists can find the hardness of metals by carrying out a scratch test. They do this by taking sheets of metal and scratching them with nails made of different metals.

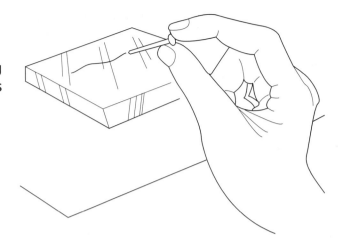

Here are some results:

Metal	Can be scratched by a copper nail	Can be scratched by a brass nail	Can be scratched by an iron nail
Sheet of copper	No	Yes	Yes
Sheet of brass	No	No	Yes
Sheet of iron	No	No	No
Sheet of lead	Yes	Yes	Yes

a. Which is the hardest metal?

_____

1

b. Which is the softest metal?

_____

1

c. What do you think would happen if you tested a sheet of aluminium foil? Write Yes or No.

Metal	Can be scratched by a copper nail	Can be scratched by a brass nail	Can be scratched by an iron nail
Aluminium foil			

3

d. What do you think would happen if you brought each of these nails or sheets of metal near to a strong magnet?

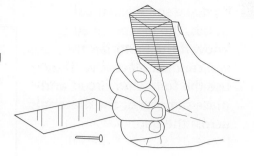

Copper _____

◯
1

Brass _____

◯
1

Iron _____

◯
1

Lead _____

◯
1

Aluminium _____

◯
1

Nickel _____

◯
1

All magnets have a north and south pole.

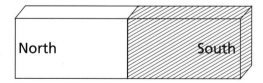

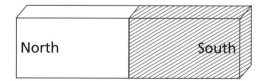

e. What happens when the different poles of a pair of magnets are held together?

	North pole	South pole
North pole		
South pole		

◯
4

TOTAL

Grouping and Classifying Materials

2 To make some electrical goods, the makers need to know if the materials they use can conduct electricity. They use the following circuit and place samples of the materials across the gap.

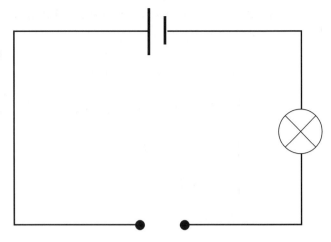

a. Write in the table of results what you would expect if you put samples of these materials across the gap in the circuit. The first one has been done for you.

Material	Put a ✔ (conducts) or a ✖ (does not conduct)
Carbon graphite pencil lead	✔
Aluminium	
Polythene	
Brass	
Wood	
Steel	
Perspex	
Copper	
Cobalt metal	

8

b. What do you call materials that do not conduct electricity?

_____

1

c. Why is carbon different from all the other materials that conduct electricity?

_____

1

TOTAL

d. Put ticks in the boxes beside those uses of carbon that rely on it conducting electricity.

Carbon brushes in motor ☐

Carbon filament light bulbs ☐

Carbon fibre fishing rods ☐

Carbon resistors ☐

Carbon in bones ☐

Carbon and zinc batteries ☐

○
3

3 Geologists can find out the names of rocks and minerals by what they look like and the colour they leave when scratched on a rough white tile (streak test).

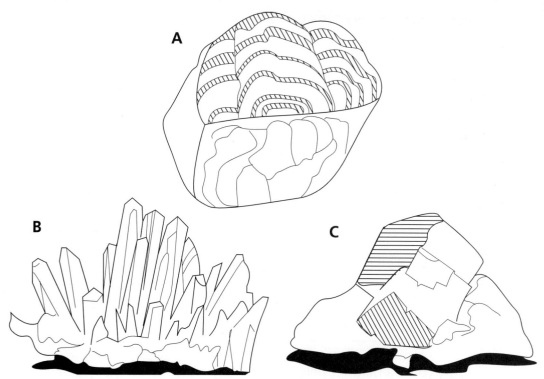

A

B   C

a. Use the following key to find the names of rocks A, B and C.

Rock A	Rock B	Rock C
Green coloured rock that leaves a light green streak.	White glassy looking rock with large crystals.	Grey black rock that leaves a grey streak.
Quite heavy rock.	Leaves a white streak.	Very heavy rock.
	Not a very heavy rock.	

Grouping and Classifying Materials

1 Rocks coloured . . . . Go to 2

   Rocks white or colourless . . . . Go to 3

2 Rocks reddish . . . . Haematite (iron ore)

   Rocks grey . . . . Go to 4

   Rocks green or yellow. . . . . Go to 5

3 Rocks look pearly . . . . Calcite

   Rocks look glassy . . . . Quartz

4 Rocks make a black streak on rough surface . . . . Graphite

   Rocks make a grey streak . . . . Galena (lead ore)

5 Rocks make light green streak . . . . Malachite (copper ore)

   Rocks make greeny brown streak . . . . Pyrite (iron ore)

Rock A is _____

Rock B is _____

Rock C is _____

b. What have all the coloured rocks got in common?

_____

_____

c. How could a magnet help to sort these rocks?

_____

_____

d. Rock B has large crystals. Is it a sedimentary, igneous or metamorphic
rock?

Rock B is _____ because _____

Circle values (left margin): 1, 1, 1, 1, 1, 2

TOTAL

4 Different plastics have properties that suit them well for the jobs they do. Here are the results from some tests on some common plastics.

Test / Material	Cut test with knife or scissors	Bend test	Float or sink test	Put into a warm oven (150°C) test	Burn with match test
Polythene	Cuts with scissors and tears easily	Bends easily	Floats	Goes soft	Burns very easily
PVC	Cuts with scissors	Bends easily	Sinks	Goes soft	Burns with difficulty
Perspex	Does not cut. Only breaks when hit with hammer	Does not bend	Sinks	Goes soft	Burns easily
Polystyrene	Cannot be cut	Does not bend, breaks easily	Sinks	Goes soft	Burns easily
Nylon	Can be cut with knife	Stiff, bends with difficulty	Sinks	Goes soft	Burns with difficulty
Melamine	Does not cut easily, makes flakes with knife	Stiff, hard, solid feel	Sinks	Stays solid	Burns with difficulty

Fill in this table with the name of the plastic you would use for each job and give **two** reasons why you have chosen it. The first one has been done for you.

Job	Your choice of plastic	Why you have chosen it
Work surface for a kitchen which will take very hot saucepans	Melamine	Does not burn Does not cut
Windscreens for motor bike		
Covering for furniture		
Bread board		
Food covering (clingfilm)		

12

TOTAL

5 Here are some properties of three materials: oak (wood), brass (metal) and nylon (plastic).

    a. Write in the words Yes or No in the empty boxes.

	Oak	Copper	Nylon
Can be cut with knife	Yes		
Can push in drawing pin			Yes
Attracted to magnet	No		No
Conducts electricity		Yes	
Rings when dropped			No
Can be beaten into flat sheets		Yes	
Can be made into a thread	No		
Looks shiny when cut			No
Burns when lit			No
Melts when put into boiling water	No		No
Floats in water		No	

20

1

1

    b. If you took exactly the same size cubes of oak, copper and nylon, which would be the heaviest?

    _____

    c. If you made exactly the same size rulers out of oak, copper and nylon, which would be the hardest to bend?

    _____

Materials and their Properties

CHANGING MATERIALS

1 When things change, sometimes they can change back to what they were like before (reversible); sometimes they remain changed forever (not reversible). Here are some changes that happen in the kitchen.

Tick the **three** sentences that describe **reversible** changes.

Flour, eggs, sugar and milk are cooked to make cakes. ☐

Ice lollies are made by freezing liquid fruit juice. ☐

A cup of soup can be made by stirring soup powder into hot water. ☐

Milk and banana are whisked to make a milk shake. ☐

Butter melts when heated in a saucepan. ☐

2 Materials can be changed in many ways.

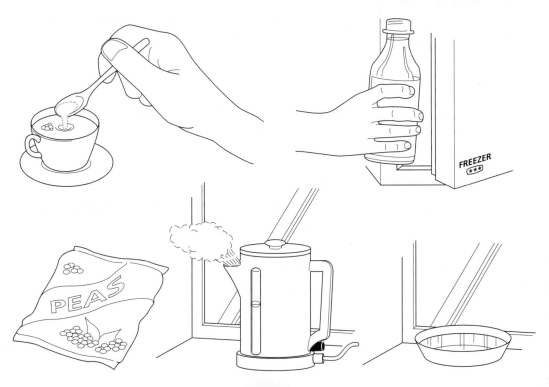

3

TOTAL

a. What would happen to a spoonful of sugar if you stirred it into a cup of tea?

_____

1

b. What would happen to the water if you left a dish of water on a window ledge for a few weeks?

_____

1

c. What would happen to a packet of frozen peas if it was taken out of the freezer for an hour?

_____

1

d. What **two** things would happen to the water in a closed bottle if it were put into a freezer for a few days?

1. _____

1

2. _____

1

e. What would happen to the steam from a kettle if it were to boil near to a cold window?

_____

1

3 Some things melt when they are warmed.

Some things burn when they are held in a candle flame.

Some things do not change when they are warmed.

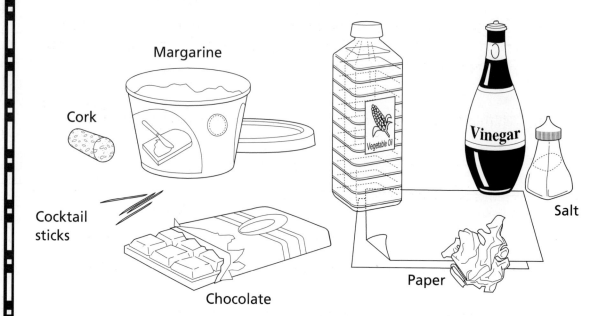

Margarine

Cork

Cocktail sticks

Chocolate

Paper

Vinegar

Salt

TOTAL

Write each of the illustrated items in its correct box below.

Things which melt when they are warmed	Things which burn in a candle flame	Things which do not change when they are warmed

4 Class 3 were trying to find out how quickly water became hot when they heated it using a candle flame.

Here is the graph they drew for the first 10 minutes of their experiment.

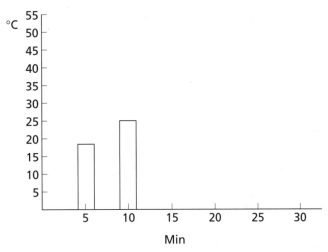

a. Draw in the rest of the graph to show how you think the temperature would change if they kept on heating the water for another 10 minutes and then a further 10 minutes.

2

b. What instrument would you use to measure how hot the water is?

1

c. What does °C mean?

2

d. What would happen to the results if the amount of water was halved?

1

TOTAL

Changing Materials

1 On this drawing which shows the water cycle in nature, write the words CONDENSATION and EVAPORATION where they describe what is going on.

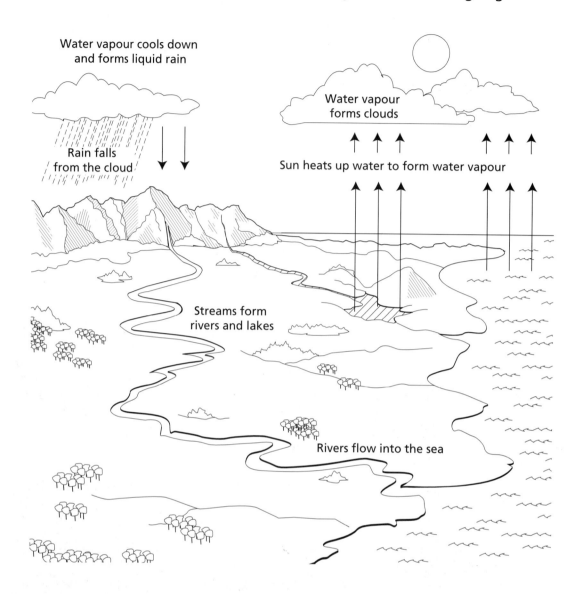

Water vapour cools down and forms liquid rain

Water vapour forms clouds

Rain falls from the cloud

Sun heats up water to form water vapour

Streams form rivers and lakes

Rivers flow into the sea

2 When Anna and her father were shopping in the supermarket they took a large packet of frozen chips from the freezer and put it into the trolley. Anna noticed that although at first the outside of the packet was dry, it soon became covered with a thin layer of water.

TOTAL

a. Where did the water come from?

_____

1

b. Put a tick in the box by the word which explains why this happened.

Evaporation ☐

Distillation ☐

Condensation ☐

Precipitation ☐

1

c. Anna could not remember where she had seen this happen before. Can you remind her? Here are some possibilities, put a tick by those which you think happen for the same reason.

A   B   C

D   E   F

A	On the outside of a cup of hot tea	☐
B	On the outside of a cold drink on a hot day	☐
C	On windows inside the car on a cold morning	☐
D	On the outside of a hot water bottle on a cold night	☐
E	On a bathroom mirror	☐
F	On the outside of a car in the rain	☐

3

TOTAL

Changing Materials

3 Class 5 were carrying out experiments to find out about how pure the water is where they live. The children tested the water from the tap by leaving some in a dish for a few days and observing what happened. After three days, they noticed that all the water had disappeared from the dish.

a. Explain why there was no water in the dish after three days.

_____

The children were amazed to find that after the water had gone there was quite a lot of solid white stuff left on the bottom of the dish. Their teacher told them that this was due to very small amounts of calcium in the water. Where there is a little calcium in the water it is said to be soft, where there is a lot the water is hard.

b. What happened when they then added some water to the white solid in the dish?

_____

The children decided to find out if water from other places was the same as theirs. They sent letters and clean plastic bottles to schools all over England to ask for samples of their tap water. When the samples arrived, Class 5 tested each one to see if calcium was present.

Here are the results for three towns:

Place	Amount of white solid left in dish
Bradford	Very little
Exeter	Quite high
Ipswich	Very high

c. Which town has the hardest water?

_____

d. Write three things that Class 5 did to make their test fair?

1. _____

2. _____

3. _____

TOTAL

72

4 Use these words to complete the three paragraphs about water. Use each word only **once**:

boils   freezes   evaporates   condenses   melts

thermometer   100°C   0°C   liquid

1. When water _____ at a temperature of
   _____ , it _____ to form water vapour.
   When the water vapour cools, it _____ into water again.

2. At _____ water _____ into ice. The
   temperature of ice can be measured using a _____ .

3. When ice is left in the air it _____ and forms
   _____ water.

4

3

2

TOTAL

1 For each of the following changes, say whether the change that is seen can be reversed (write **R**) or not (write **N**). Explain why.

A. burning candle (**R** or **N**) _____

because _____

_____

B. setting jelly (**R** or **N**) _____

because _____

_____

C. steam condensing into water (**R** or **N**) _____

because _____

_____

D. match burning (**R** or **N**) _____

because _____

_____

E. clay hardening in kiln (**R** or **N**) _____

because _____

_____

F. gas jet burning on cooker (**R** or **N**) _____

because _____

_____

12

TOTAL

74

2 Some ice was taken out of the freezer and crushed in a food processor. The crushed ice was put in a bowl and left in a warm room. This graph shows how the temperature in the bowl changed over the first hour.

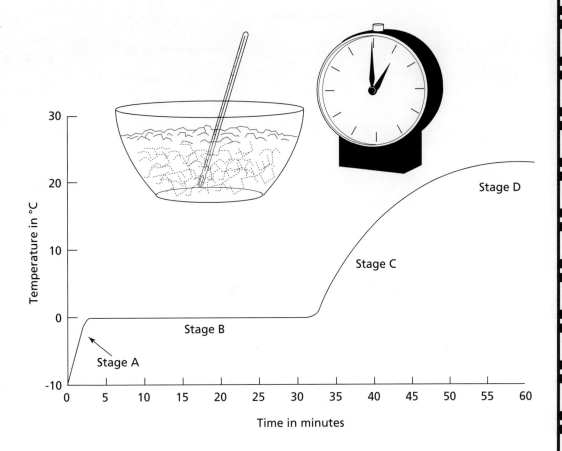

a. What is happening to the crushed ice at Stage A?

_____

◯ 2

b. What is happening to the crushed ice at Stage B?

_____

◯ 1

c. What would the contents of the bowl look like at Stage C?

_____

◯ 2

d. What is happening to the temperature at Stage D and why is this happening?

_____ because _____

_____

◯ 2

TOTAL

◻ 75

3 This diagram shows a water cycle.

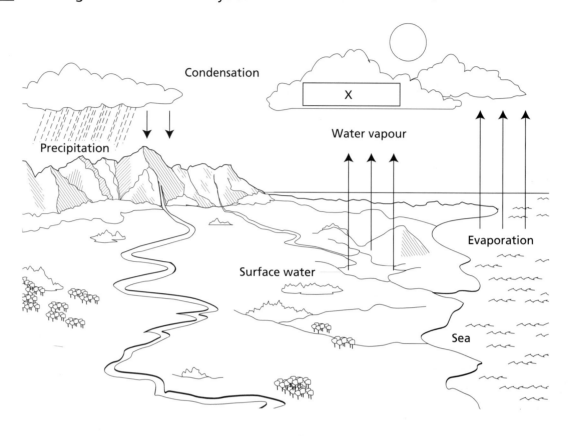

a. How does the water from the sea evaporate?

1

_____

b. What should be written in box X?

1

_____

c. What is the common name for precipitation?

1

_____

d. What effect would weather conditions such as fog, low temperatures and no wind, have on evaporation from the sea?

1

_____

e. What force moves the surface water so that it flows into the sea?

1

_____

TOTAL

4 Class 6 were measuring puddles to see how they changed size during the day.

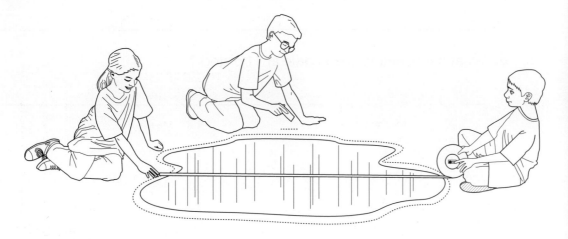

a. What happens to the water in a puddle when it dries up?

_____

1

b. Write down **three** things that Class 6 found affect the way puddles get smaller.

1. _____

2. _____

3. _____

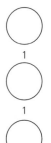

1

1

1

Class 6 drew a graph to show how the size of a puddle changed on a cold day.

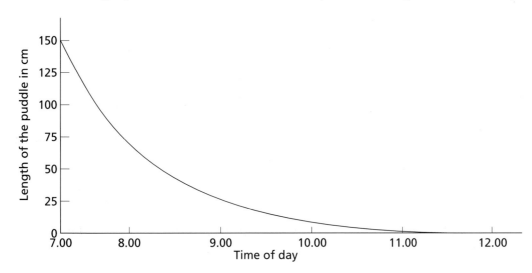

c. Draw a different line on the graph to show how the puddle would have changed on a hot day.

2

TOTAL

1

1

d. Explain why the line you have drawn is different.

_____

e. What happened to the puddle at 11 o'clock?

_____

TOTAL

Materials and their Properties

SEPARATING MIXTURES OF MATERIALS

1 By using a magnifier you can see the bits which make up soil. They are different sizes varying from heavy stones, through pieces of sand to very fine, light clay and dust (silt).

Some soil was shaken up with water in a jar and then left to stand. After a few days everything had settled and looked like this.

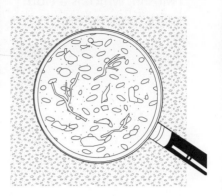

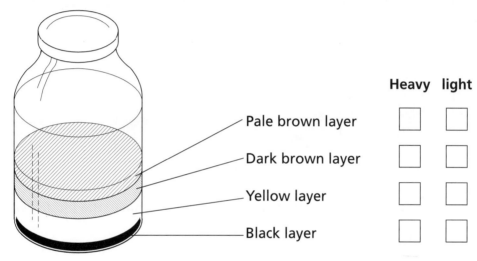

Heavy light

Pale brown layer ☐ ☐

Dark brown layer ☐ ☐

Yellow layer ☐ ☐

Black layer ☐ ☐

4

a. Look at the drawing and tick the layers which are made up of the heavy bits of soil and the layers which are the light bits.

b. If you put some soil in a sieve, which bits would pass through and which bits would not? Put a tick in the correct boxes.

	Would pass through sieve	Would not pass through sieve
Pale brown layer	☐	☐
Dark brown layer	☐	☐
Yellow layer	☐	☐
Black layer	☐	☐

4

TOTAL

Separating Mixtures of Materials

2 Class 3 were doing experiments to make muddy water clean.
They poured some muddy sea water through three different kinds of cloth.

Muslin, which is a cloth with loose weave	Curtain net, which is loosely woven	Silk with a very close weave
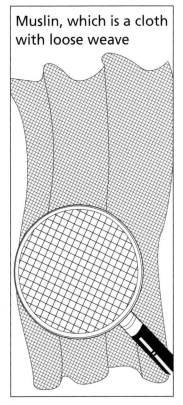	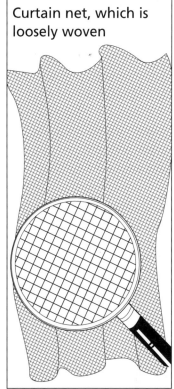	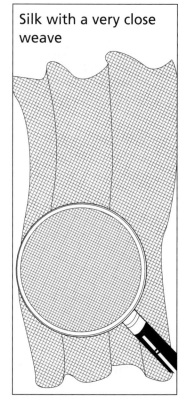

a. Which sort of cloth would be the best to make the muddy water clear?

_____

b. What happens to the mud in the muddy water as it goes through the cloth?

_____

c. Even though the muddy water has been through the cloth, why must you not drink it?

_____

d. Which one of these processes could provide water that you could drink?

Tick **one** box

Leave the muddy water for a few days and let the mud settle ☐

Boil the muddy water and collect the steam ☐

Boil the muddy water, then pass it through a filter paper ☐

Put a sponge into the muddy water and squeeze out the liquid ☐

1

1

1

1

TOTAL

3 Put a tick in the box by those materials which will dissolve in water.

Alka Seltzer tablet ☐

Piece of chalk ☐

Sugar lump ☐

Knob of butter ☐

Grains of salt ☐

Grains of sand ☐

3

TOTAL

1 When Arran made a cup of coffee, he used a coffee filter to separate the coffee grounds from the liquid coffee.

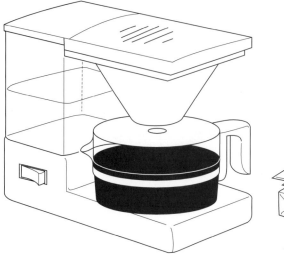 

a. Explain why the coffee grounds did not go through the filter paper.

_____

b. Tick **one** scientific word that describes what Arran did to the coffee.

Distilled it ☐

Condensed it ☐

Filtered it ☐

Evaporated it ☐

c. Tick the boxes of other mixtures that can be separated in the same way.

Tea leaves from tea ☐

Oil and water ☐

Salt and water ☐

Sand and water ☐

2 In Turkey, children make a drink called *sherbet* by dissolving a spoonful of lemonade powder in water.

1

1

2

a. Write down **two** ways they could make the powder dissolve more quickly.

1. _____

2. _____

1

1

b. If they wanted to get the lemonade powder back again, which **one** of the following methods could they use?

Tick **one** box

Filter the sherbet and collect the powder from the filter paper ☐

Evaporate the water and collect the powder from the dish ☐

Dip filter paper in the sherbet; the water will be sucked up, and the powder left in the dish ☐

Pass an electric current through the sherbet ☐

1

3 Anne makes coffee by putting a spoonful of coffee granules in a cup with 100 cm³ of hot milk and then adding sugar to make it sweet.

Anne likes to dip a biscuit in her coffee before eating it. Sometimes the biscuit gets soft and falls into the coffee. Anne has to use a spoon to fish out the biscuit.

TOTAL

$\bigcirc$ 5

a. Complete the following sentences by ticking either Soluble or Insoluble each time:

Tick **one** box for each sentence

	Soluble	Insoluble
The coffee granules are ____?____ in the hot milk.	☐	☐
The cup is ____?____ in hot milk.	☐	☐
The sugar is ____?____ in the cup of coffee.	☐	☐
The biscuit is ____?____ in the cup of coffee.	☐	☐
The spoon is ____?____ in hot milk.	☐	☐

Anne wanted to make coffee for her friends. She put one spoonful of granules into a jug and added 400 cm³ of hot milk, enough for four cups. When she poured it out, the coffee was a lighter colour and did not taste the same.

$\bigcirc$ 1

b. Why was this?

_____

Anne tried to make coffee by adding the granules to cold milk. She found that the granules did not dissolve very well.

$\bigcirc$ 1

c. What could she do to make them dissolve better?

_____

TOTAL

Separating Mixtures of Materials

1 Scientists use a nest of soil sieves to test different soils. Each of the four sieves has a mesh that is finer than the one above. After a sample of soil has been dried, it is put into the nest and shaken and the mass of soil in each of the four sieves is measured.

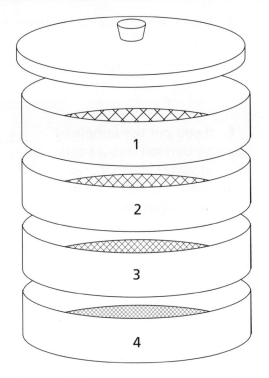

Here are the results for samples of soil taken from a river bank and a garden:

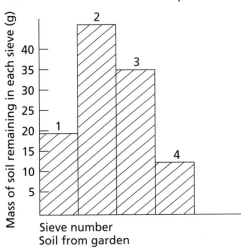

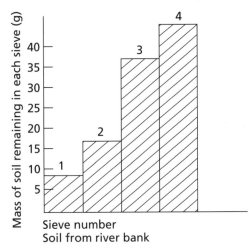

a. Which of the two samples of soil has the most clay?

_____

b. Explain your answer.

_____

c. Which soil would let water pass through it easily?

_____

d. Explain your answer.

_____

TOTAL

○ 1

e. How do scientists make sure their soil tests are fair?

_____

_____

○ 2

f. If you put the sample of garden soil into a bottle of water, shake it and leave it to stand for an hour, what will it look like?

Draw what you think it will look like.

○ 1

g. Here are the results of leaving a dishful of each soil over a weekend:

Soil	Mass on Friday measured in grams	Mass on Monday measured in grams
River bank	250	220
Garden	250	180

Explain why the mass of both soils has decreased over the weekend

_____

_____

2 Here is a graph showing the solubility of four chemicals at different temperatures. The solubility is the mass of each chemical that will dissolve in 100 grams of water.

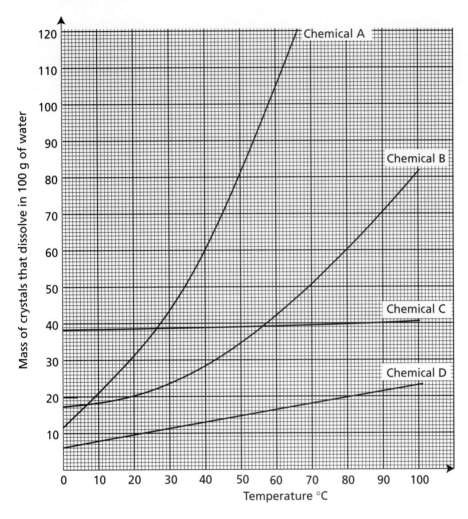

Using the graph, answer the following questions:

a. What mass of chemical A will dissolve at 10°C?

_____

2

b. What mass of chemical D will dissolve at 58°C?

_____

2

c. At what temperature will 39 grams of chemicals B and C dissolve?

_____

2

d. What will happen to chemical C if you add 60 grams at 80°C?

_____

_____

1

TOTAL

Separating Mixtures of Materials

a. Draw lines to link the following pieces of scientific equipment with the jobs they do:

1.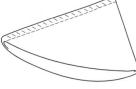

    a. Measures temperature

2.

    b. Holds filter paper

3.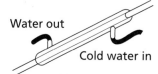

Water out

Cold water in

    c. Evaporates liquids from mixtures of solids and liquids

4.

    d. Filters solid materials

5.

    e. Condenses hot vapours

b. Put a tick against the correct ending to the sentence:
Tick **one** box

We filter things to separate ...

... solute from a solvent

... insoluble materials from each other

... insoluble materials from liquids

... soluble materials from each other

c. How can you separate this mixture of sand and water without using any scientific apparatus?

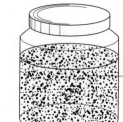

Sandy water

_____

_____

5

1

3

TOTAL

Physical Processes

ELECTRICITY

1 Jason tried to make a circuit so that the doorbell sounds, but it will not work.

Put a tick by the reason why the bell will not sound.

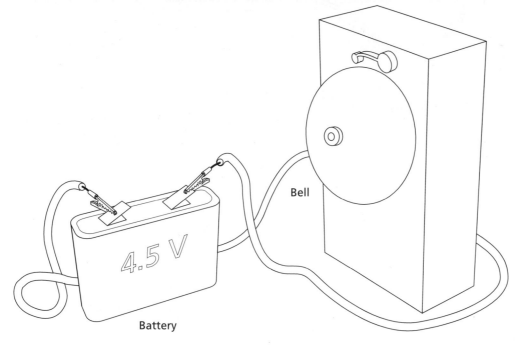

Bell

4.5 V

Battery

Tick **one** box

The battery is the wrong way round ☐

The wires are bent ☐

The crocodile clips are too tight ☐

One crocodile clip is not connected ☐

1

2 This kind of battery is used to make a bicycle lamp work.

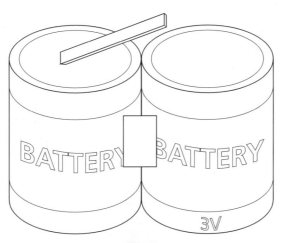

BATTERY BATTERY

3V

Put ticks by those circuits which will light the bulb.

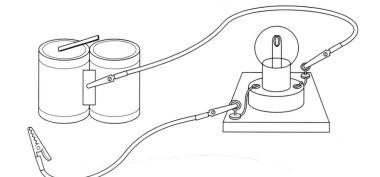

A

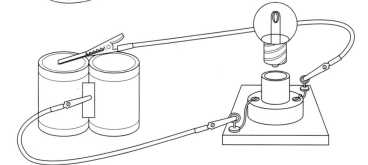

B

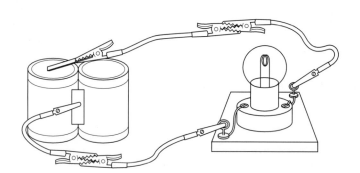

C

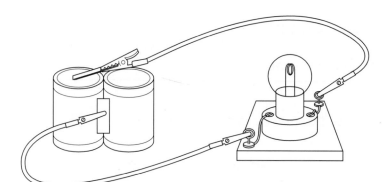

D

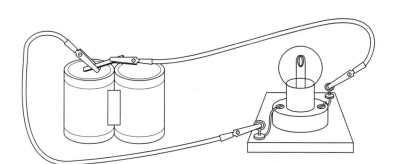

E

2

TOTAL

90

3 Julia and Casey were using batteries, wires and bulbs to make festival lights. Casey found that her lights were not as bright as Julia's.

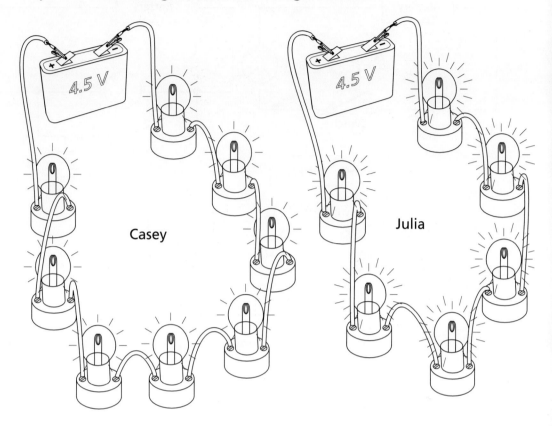

Write down the reason for this.

1

_____

_____

TOTAL

1 Susan and Jamil made circuits using switches, bulbs and buzzers.

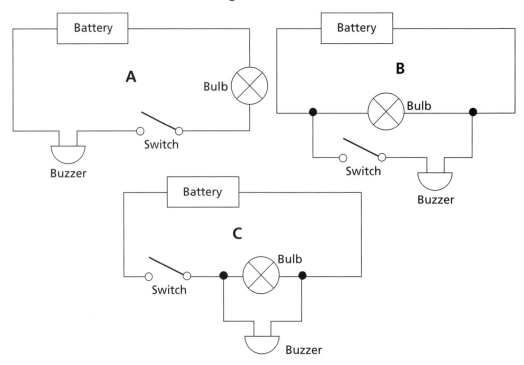

a. Which circuit can switch both bulb and buzzer on and let the buzzer sound even when the bulb is unscrewed and taken out?

_____

b. Which circuit allows the bulb and the buzzer to be switched on only when both are connected?

_____

c. Which circuit allows the buzzer to be switched on and off and the bulb to stay on all of the time?

_____

1

1

1

2 Alison has made a circuit with

a battery ─┤├─,

a bulb ⊗,

a motor Ⓜ and

two switches ─o╱o─ .

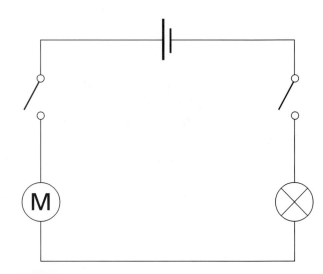

a. How many switches must be pressed to make the bulb light up?

_____

1

b. How many switches must be pressed to make the motor work?

_____

1

3 Here are two drawings of circuits and five circuit diagrams.

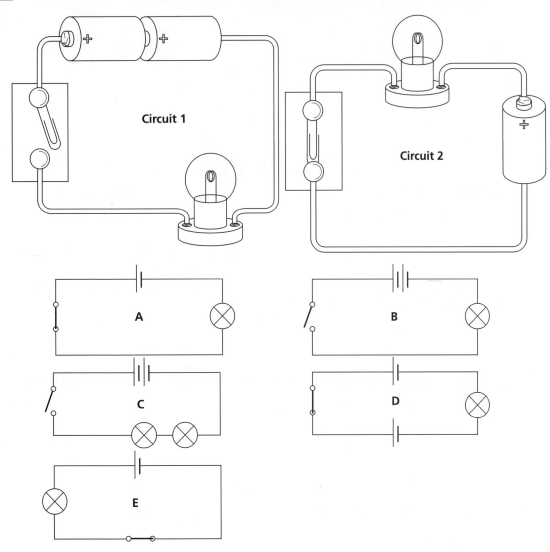

a. Put a tick by the circuit diagram which shows **Circuit 1**.

A ☐   B ☐   C ☐   D ☐   E ☐

1

b. Put a tick by the circuit diagram which shows **Circuit 2**.

A ☐   B ☐   C ☐   D ☐   E ☐

1

1 Anna connected up the circuit drawn below.

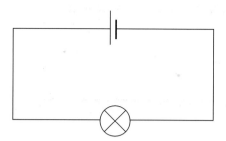

The bulb was very dim. Her friend Gemma suggested three circuits which could be used to make the bulb brighter.

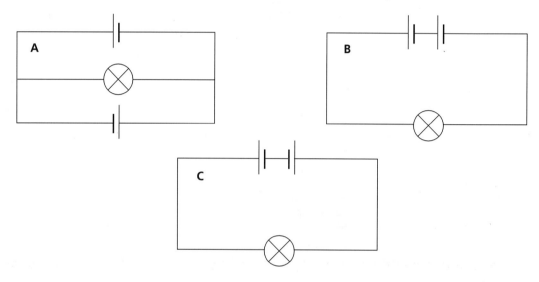

a. Which is the correct circuit to use, A, B or C?

_____

Anna set up this circuit and used an ammeter to measure the current in the circuit.

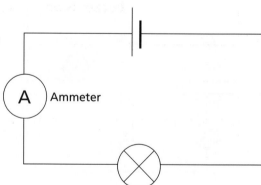

She then placed another bulb in the circuit and measured the current again.

b. How did the ammeter reading for the circuit with two bulbs compare with that for the circuit with one bulb?

_____

○
1

2 Here are five circuit diagrams containing a bulb ⊗, a buzzer ⊲ and two switches —o͞ o—, —o͞ o—.

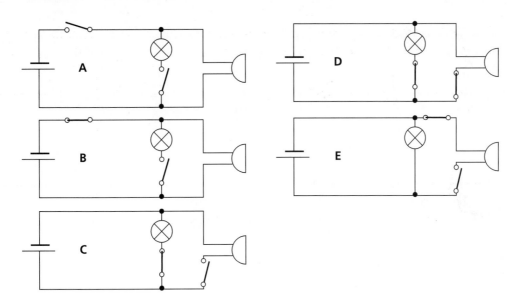

Look carefully at the circuit diagrams and tick the correct box to show what is happening in each circuit.

○
5

Circuit	Only the buzzer is on	Only the bulb is on	Both the buzzer and bulb are on	The buzzer and bulb are both off
A				
B				
C				
D				
E				

Physical Processes

FORCES AND MOTION

1 Class 4 were finding out about how different magnets attract metal. Here are the results of the experiments they did to find out how many paper clips each magnet would hold.

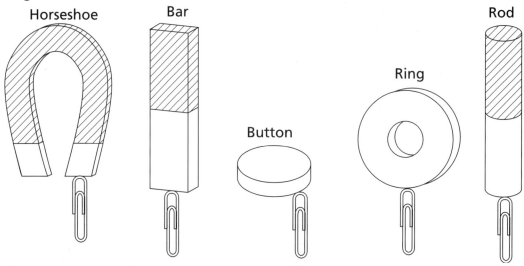

Magnet	Horseshoe	Bar	Button	Ring	Rod
Number of paper clips	24	28	27	64	28

a. Which magnet has the greatest force of attraction for paper clips?

_____

Some children in the class held a bar magnet in each hand and slowly brought them together.

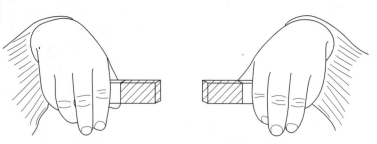

b. Complete the sentences below describing whether they felt the force of the magnets pushing or pulling their hands.

Write push or pull

Held a north pole near to a north pole _____

Held a south pole near to a south pole _____

Held a south pole near to a north pole _____

1

1

1

1

TOTAL

2 Springs are used to do many jobs because of the pushing or pulling forces they can give.

For each of these uses, say whether the spring does its job using pushing or pulling forces.

Write pushing
or pulling

Spring to close door   _____

1

Springs in a mattress   _____

1

Spring in a ball pen   _____

1

Spring in kitchen scales   _____

1

Spring in a pinball game   _____

1

3 Some children are playing on the slide in the park. They sit on different things and see who can slide the fastest. Jane sits on a rough door mat, Justin sits on a smooth metal tray and Jamie uses a sheet of cardboard.

TOTAL

a. Who will take the longest to slide down to the bottom?

_____

b. Who will slide down the quickest?

_____

c. What affects how quickly the children can slide down?

_____

4 If you use a straw to blow a table-tennis ball you can affect the way it moves.

a. Fill in the table by putting a tick in the box which best describes what will happen to the table-tennis ball.

	It goes more quickly	It goes more slowly	It stops rolling	It changes direction
It is rolling towards you				
It is rolling away from you				
It is rolling across a table				
Somebody is blowing from the other side (blow football)				

Level markers: 1, 1, 1, 4

TOTAL

1

b. When you play blow football, what will affect the way that the ball moves?

_____

TOTAL

Forces and Motion

1 Class 5 made parachutes and tested them to find what affected the speed at which they fell.

They took pieces of cloth of different sizes to make the parachutes and on each one tied a 50 g mass. They dropped each parachute from the top of a ladder and timed how long it took to reach the floor.

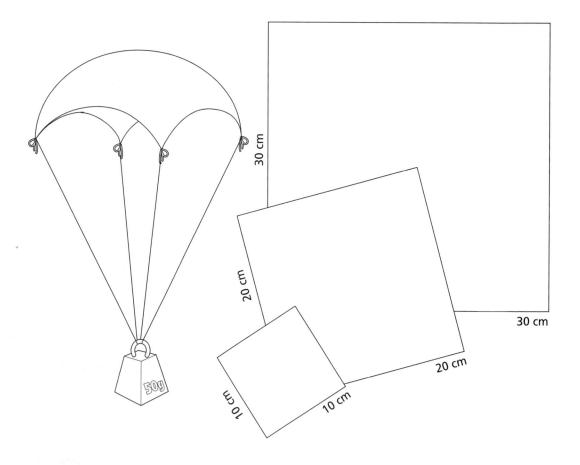

30 cm

30 cm

20 cm

20 cm

10 cm

10 cm

a. Which parachute would take the longest to reach the floor?

_____

b. What force is making the parachute fall?

_____

c. What force prevents the parachute from falling very quickly?

_____

d. Give two ways Class 5 made their tests fair.

1. _____

2. _____

1

1

1

1

1

TOTAL

Forces and Motion

2 Paul and Leslie carried out experiments to see how a radio-operated car with large rubber tyres would climb a slope. They let the car climb up a ramp which was covered with different surfaces and measured the time it took to travel on the different surfaces.

a. How could Paul and Leslie make sure their test is fair?

1. _____

2. _____

b. They covered the ramp with smooth plastic, rough sandpaper and carpet. On which surface do you think the car took longest to climb?

_____

c. What is the force that helps the tyres on the car to grip the surface?

_____

3 Jessica is finding out about the compression of a bed spring. She places metal weights on the spring and measures how long the spring is.

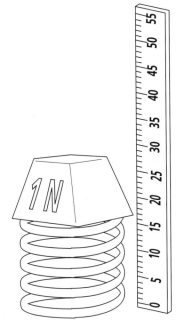

1

1

1

1

TOTAL

Forces and Motion

Weight on bed spring	Length of spring
1 newton (N)	15.0 cm
2 newtons	14.0 cm
3 newtons	13.5 cm
4 newtons	12.5 cm
5 newtons	12.0 cm

The first of her results has been plotted on a line graph.

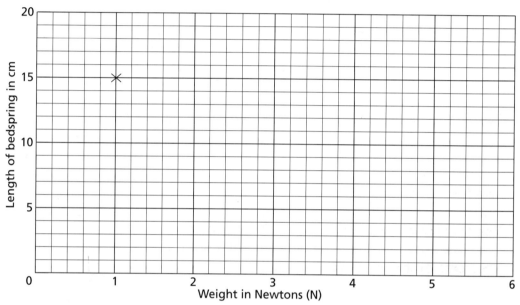

a. Plot the other four points on the graph and draw a line that best fits these points.

b. How long was the bed spring without any weights on it?

_____

c. On this drawing, draw arrows to show the forces affecting the weight.

5

1

2

TOTAL

4 A man is pushing a wheelbarrow loaded with soil. The arrows on the drawing show some of the forces.

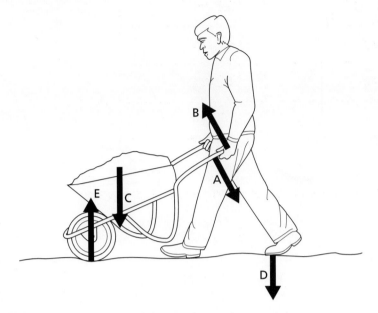

Tick the box which shows the correct arrow for each force:

	A	B	C	D	E
The force of gravity on the soil	☐	☐	☐	☐	☐
The force of the man on the wheelbarrow handles	☐	☐	☐	☐	☐
The force of the ground on the wheel	☐	☐	☐	☐	☐

3

1 On firework night, a rocket in a bottle is ready to be launched. The blue touch paper is lit, the rocket fuel explodes and an upward force is produced on the rocket.

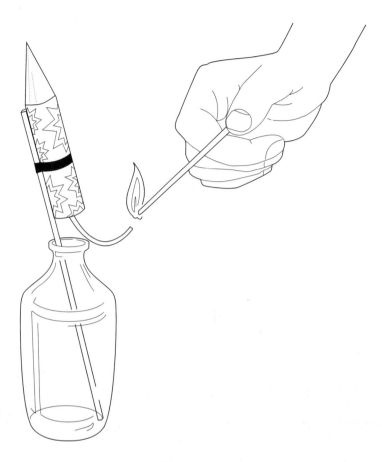

a. If the upward force is less than the weight of the rocket, what will happen to the movement of the rocket?

_____

b. If the upward force equals the weight of the rocket, what will happen to the movement of the rocket?

_____

c. If the upward force is greater than the weight of the rocket, what will happen to the movement of the rocket?

_____

d. What scientific units are used to measure the weight of the rocket?

_____

e. What units are used to measure the mass of the rocket?

_____

1

1

1

1

1

TOTAL

2 The Highway Code has a table which shows the distance it takes to stop a car when travelling at different speeds:

Car speed in miles per hour	Stopping distance in metres
20	12
30	23
40	36
50	53
60	73
70	96

a. Plot a graph of stopping distance against car speed.

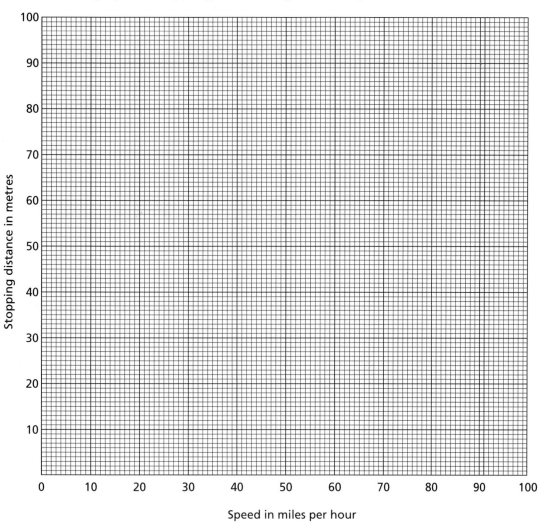

6

b. The speed limit in parts of USA is 55 miles per hour. What is the stopping distance for a car travelling at that speed?

_____

1

TOTAL

○
1

○
2

○
1

c. Drivers are advised to allow at least double the stopping distance in wet weather. Why do you think this is?

_____

d. Describe **two** frictional forces which help to stop a car?

_____

_____

e. Here is a drawing of a tyre in contact with the road when the car is not moving. Draw arrows to show two forces on the tyre.

_____

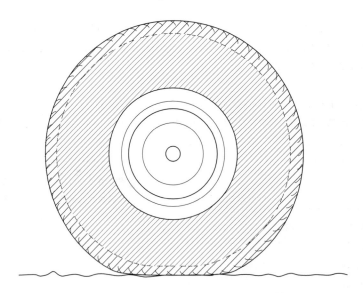

3 Diving bells are used to explore the floor of the ocean. They have a television camera on board and can move using their own motors. They are moved by remote control by the scientists on the ship. They are lowered into and taken out of the water using a crane.

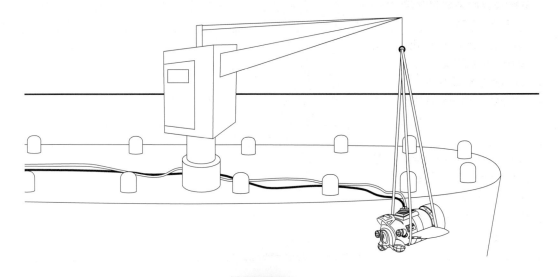

TOTAL

Each diving bell weighs 60000 N. The upthrust of sea water on the diving bell is 20500 N.

For each of the following questions, put a tick if you think the answer is Sinks, Rises or Does not move.

	Sinks	Rises	Does not move
What happens to the diving bell when the crane lifts with a force of 39500 N?	☐	☐	☐
What happens to the diving bell when the crane lifts with a force of 20500 N?	☐	☐	☐
What happens to the diving bell when the crane lifts with a force of 40000 N	☐	☐	☐

3

4 The table contains four drawings of a small yacht sailing in the sea. The yacht has a motor which can be used to help it move. The weather and sea conditions are described.

For each of the conditions described, say what happens to the movement of the yacht and list as many forces as you can which affect this movement.

Conditions	Describe the movement of the yacht	List the forces affecting the movement
There is a wind **A** blowing from behind the sail and the sea is calm.		
There is still a wind, **B** but the tide has started to turn and there is a current in the opposite direction to the wind.		
The wind is blowing, **C** there is still a current and the motor is turned on.		
The wind becomes **D** stronger, the tide slows down and the motor is kept running.		

3

3

3

3

TOTAL

Physical Processes

LIGHT AND SOUND

1 Kitchen foil looks shiny.

Why does the kitchen foil look shiny?

Tick **one** box

The foil gives out light ☐

The foil reflects light ☐

The foil lets light pass through ☐

The foil is smooth ☐

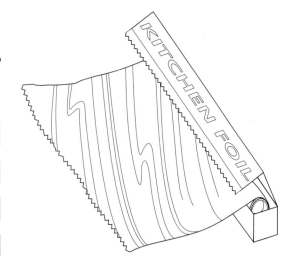

1

2 Some children were finding out about light. They lit a candle and placed it behind a sheet of thick cardboard. In the middle of the cardboard was a small hole. The children then stood around the cardboard sheet like this:

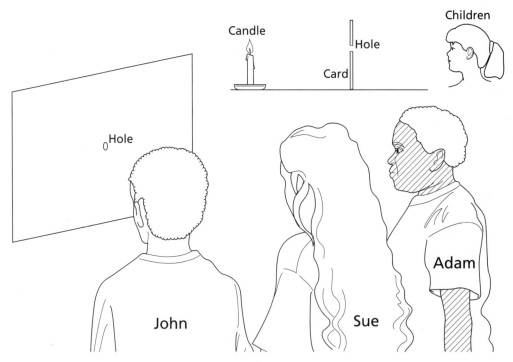

a. Which one of the children could see the candle flame most clearly?

_____

1

b. Why could the other two children not see the candle flame so well?

_____

1

TOTAL

3 These three groups of children are working on the school field. Their teacher blows the whistle to call them in.

a. Which group cannot hear the whistle so well?

_____

◯
1

b. Explain why some children can hear a louder sound than others.

_____

◯
1

c. How could the teacher make sure all the children can hear her?

_____

◯
1

4 Sam shone the light from a torch into a mirror so that it made a bright spot on the wall.

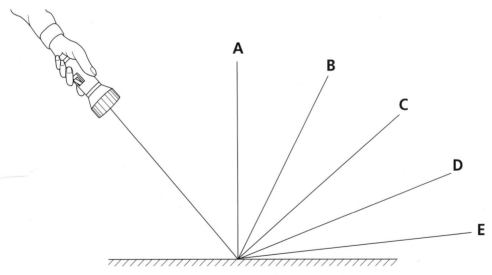

Where on the wall would the bright spot be found: A, B, C, D or E?

_____

◯
1

TOTAL

5 Alan is playing a drum. He puts some rice on the drum then hits the skin with a beater.

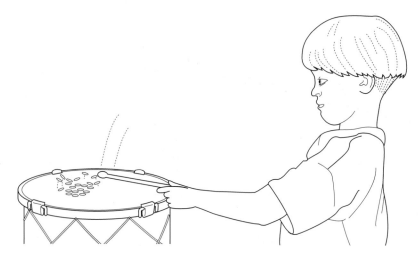

a. What happens to the rice?

_____

1

b. What happens to the rice as Alan hits the drum harder and harder?

_____

1

Light and Sound

1 Musical instruments make a sound when a part of them vibrates.
For each of these instruments, put an X where the vibration makes a sound

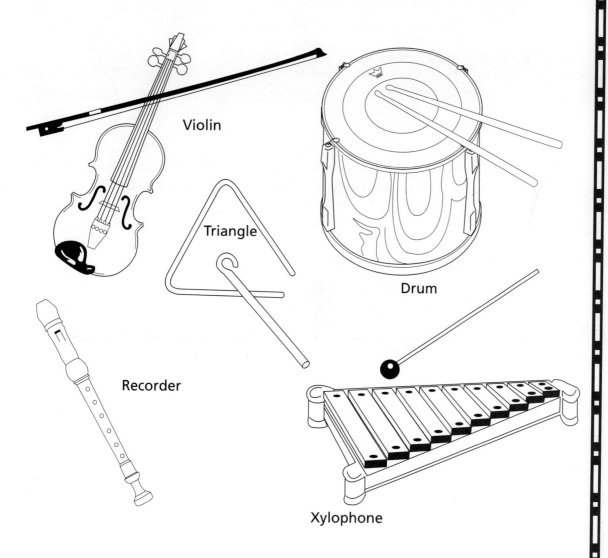

Violin

Triangle

Drum

Recorder

Xylophone

5

2 Sean and Kevin used two plastic pots and string to make a string telephone.
Later, they changed the string for some metal wire and tried again. They also
tried some nylon fishing line.

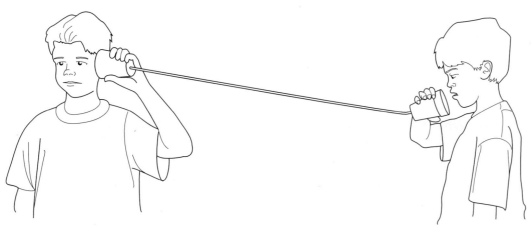

TOTAL

a. Will all of these materials make a good telephone? Explain why you think this.

_____

○ 2

b. How can they make this a fair test?

_____

○ 1

3 Class 6 were making shadow portraits using a bright light from the projector and large sheets of paper. Alison is sitting in front of the screen.

a. Where will the shadow of her head (not her shoulders) be on the paper?

○ 1

Tick **one** box

A to D

B to F

A to E

A to F

B to E

b. What **two** things could she do to make her shadow appear smaller on the screen?

1. _____

○ 1

2. _____

○ 1

TOTAL

112

c. Explain why shadows of the head are formed.

_____

_____

◯
1

4 Ali and Jane are trying to arrange **two** mirrors so that the bright light beam from a projector will travel round a corner and shine on a wall.

Classroom

Wall
A

Projector
pointing
at Wall B

Wall
B

On this plan of the classroom, use a ruler to draw in:

a. where they must put the two mirrors to get the light beam on the part of the wall marked A, and
b. the path taken by the light beam.

◯
2

1 Mary used a small mirror to look behind herself at some shapes on the classroom wall.

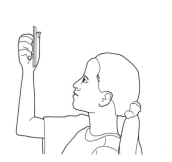

a. Look at this drawing and say which shape Mary could see best.

_____

b. Use a ruler to draw the ray of light to explain your answer. Use an arrow to show which way the ray of light is moving.

_____

_____

2 Here is a picture of a guitar.

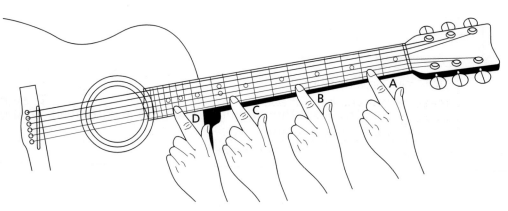

a. If you wanted to produce a note with the highest pitch, would you put your finger on the string at A, B, C or D?

_____

b. Describe another way of producing a high-pitched sound.

_____

c. How would you produce a louder sound from the strings?

_____

1

2

1

1

1

TOTAL

d. How do the guitar strings make a sound and how does that sound reach your ears?

_____

_____

_____

3

3 Draw a line between each of these statements about light and the correct scientific word that describes them.

1
| Light can pass through this material and you can see through it. |

a
| Opaque |

2
| Light cannot pass through this material and you cannot see through it. |

b
| Luminous |

3
| Light can pass through this material but you cannot see through it. |

c
| Translucent |

4
| Light cannot pass through this material but bounces off. |

d
| Transparent |

5
| Light is produced by this object, e.g. the Sun. |

e
| Reflective |

5

TOTAL

4 Here is some information about the speed of sound.

> The speed of sound is measured in metres per second (m/s).
>
> Sound travels through different materials at different speeds:
>
> | | |
> |---|---|
> | rubber | 54 m/s |
> | cold air | 330 m/s |
> | warm air | 350 m/s |
> | hydrogen | 1286 m/s |
> | fresh water | 1410 m/s |
> | sea water | 1540 m/s |
> | wood | 3500 m/s |
> | copper | 3650 m/s |
> | glass | 4000 m/s |
> | steel | 5060 m/s |
> | granite | 6000 m/s |

Use this information and for each of these statements about sound tick **True** or **False**.

		True	False
A	'String' telephones work better using copper wire than steel wire.	☐	☐
B	It is easier to hear underwater in a lake than in the sea.	☐	☐
C	It is easier to hear the sound of a ticking clock through a balloon filled with air than one filled with hydrogen.	☐	☐
D	It is easier to hear distant sounds in summer than in winter.	☐	☐
E	Sound travels more quickly in solids than in liquids.	☐	☐

5

TOTAL

Physical Processes

THE EARTH AND BEYOND

1 Here is a drawing of the Earth as seen from space.

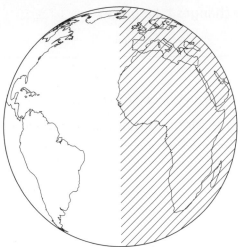

a. Draw an arrow on the picture to show from which direction the Sun is shining on to the Earth.

b. Here are four sentences about the Earth, Moon and Sun.
Tick if you think they are **True** or **False**.

	True	False
A The Moon is bigger in size than the Sun.	☐	☐
B The Moon moves round the Earth once every month.	☐	☐
C The Sun moves around the Earth once every year.	☐	☐
D The Earth, Moon and Sun are all spheres (like balls).	☐	☐

1

4

2 These pictures show the Sun's position in the sky at different times of the day.
The pictures also show the shadow of a boy standing in the playground.

TOTAL

a. Write **two** changes in the shadow as the day goes on.

1. _____

2. _____

b. Why do these changes take place?

_____

3 The drawings show the Moon as it appears on different nights in the month.

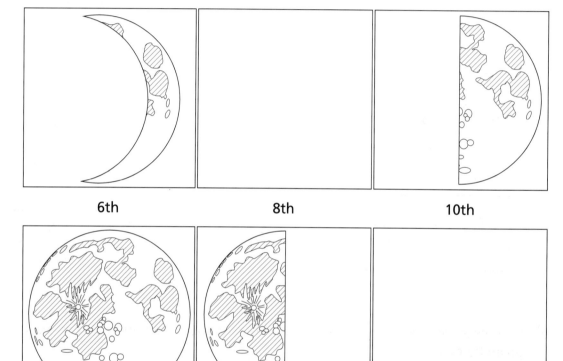

6th	8th	10th

17th	24th	27th

a. Draw what the Moon looks like on the 8th of the month.

b. Draw what the Moon looks like on the 27th of the month.

TOTAL

1 In our part of the Solar system, the Earth and the Moon move around the Sun.

Draw lines to match each sentence with the correct numbers in the box.

1
| The number of days it takes for the Moon to orbit the Earth |

a | 1 |

2
| The number of days it takes for the Earth to orbit the Sun |

b | 24 |

3
| The number of hours it takes for the Earth to spin once on its axis |

c | 28 |

4
| The extra days there are in a leap year |

d | 365 |

4

2 Complete the following sentences by choosing the correct words from those given below:

Earth   Sun   reflects   orbit

The Moon shines because it _____ light that comes from

the _____ .

Seen from the Moon, the Earth shines because it _____ light

that comes from the _____ .

4

119

TOTAL

3 On the drawing, the Sun is shown where it would be seen early in the morning at 7 o'clock.

7 am   10 am   Lunch time   3 pm   5 pm   7 pm

   a. For each of the other times given, draw in where you would expect to see the Sun.

   b. At what time would the shadow of the tree be shortest?

   _____

5

1

4 This drawing shows the Sun as it appears in the sky at 12 o'clock lunch time on 21st March.

◯ The Sun at lunch time

On the drawing, draw circles to show where you would expect to see the Sun at lunchtime on:

   a. 21st December (label it Dec).

   b. 21st June (label it Jun).

2

1 Here are drawings showing the phases of the Moon as seen at different times during the month. They are not in the correct order.

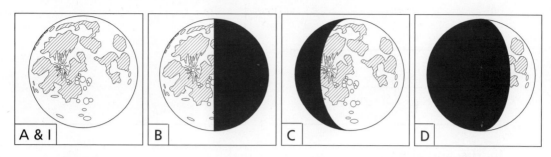

Full Moon   _____   _____   _____

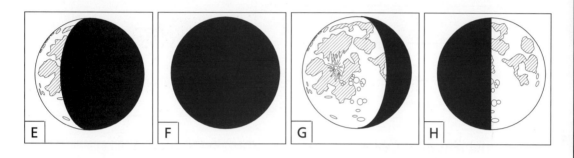

_____   _____   _____   _____

Put the letters on the pictures in the correct order and give each picture a label from the list of words given below. The first and last phases have been done for you and you can use the words more than once.

Correct order of pictures _____

Last quarter   Full Moon   New   Crescent   First quarter   Gibbous

2 Use words and diagrams of the Earth, Moon and Sun to explain:

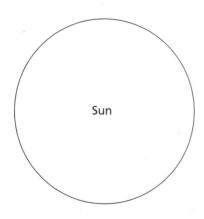

7

7

TOTAL

a. the length of a day.

_____

_____

_____

_____

b. day and night.

_____

_____

_____

_____

c. the length of a year.

_____

_____

_____

_____

d. the position of the Sun in the sky at different times of the year.

_____

_____

_____

_____

e. why the Moon appears to change shape.

_____

_____

_____

_____

1

1

1

1

1

TOTAL

1

f. why we see the same face of the
Moon each night.

_____

_____

_____

_____

123

INSTRUCTIONS

Read this carefully

Answers

Write your answers on the lines provided.

For some questions you may need to draw an answer, for others you simply put a tick or cross in the correct box(es).

You have 35 minutes to complete this test.

TEST 1

1 Flowers

Here is a drawing showing some parts of a lily flower which has been pulled apart. The name of each part is given.

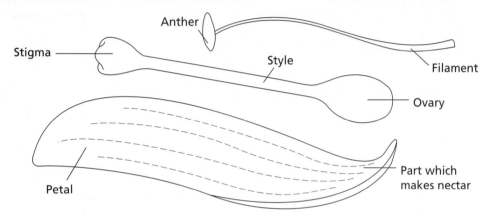

a. Which part produces pollen?

_____

b. On which part does a visiting insect leave pollen?

_____

c. Why does a part of the petal make nectar?

_____

d. Which part of the flower will make the seed?

_____

1

1

1

Sc2

1

2 Naming flowers

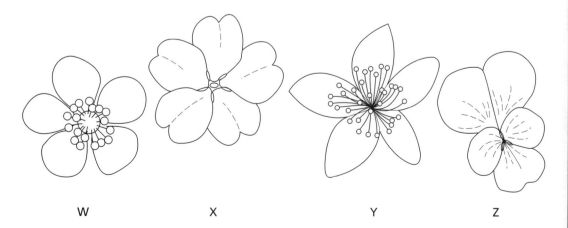

W   X   Y   Z

Use this key to find the names of flowers W, X, Y and Z

A   Petals all the same size . . . . Go to B
    Some petals larger than others . . . . Violet

B   Flower has 5 stamens. . . . . Primrose
    Flower has more than 5 stamens . . . . Go to C

C   Flower has 1 carpel . . . . St. John's Wort
    Flower has more than 1 carpel . . . . Strawberry

Write the letter W, X, Y or Z against the name of the flower.

The strawberry is flower   _____

The St. John's Wort is flower   _____

The primrose is flower   _____

The violet is flower   _____

Sc2

4

3 Smoking and health

Cigarette smoke contains the drug nicotine to which smokers become
addicted. It also contains tar which can cause lung cancer and heart disease.
On the side of a packet of cigarettes are written the amounts of nicotine and
tar. The Government also writes a warning to smokers advising them of the
dangers of smoking.

Here are some Government figures:

	Amount of tar in one cigarette (mg)	Amount of nicotine in one cigarette (mg)
Brand A	3	0.3
Brand B	6	0.6
Brand C	9	0.6
Brand D	12	1.1
Brand E	14	0.9

a. Which brand will give the greatest risk of lung cancer?

_____

1

b. Which brand could be the most addictive?

_____

1

On the back of Brand B is written:

> Warning by HM Government
> SMOKING DURING PREGNANCY CAN
> SERIOUSLY DAMAGE YOUR BABY'S HEALTH
> AND MAY LEAD TO PREMATURE DEATH

c. What advice would you give to an expectant mother who smokes?

_____

4 **Making a cup of tea**

a. On this drawing of a glass kettle being used to make a cup of tea, write the words gas, liquid or solid in the correct parts.

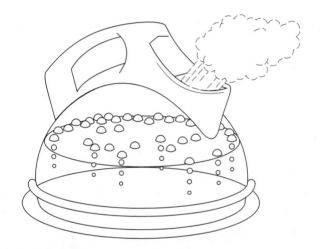

If hot water is added to a teapot with some tea leaves, you have to use a tea strainer when you pour the tea in a cup. If you use a tea bag, you do not need a strainer.

b. Why do you **not** need a strainer when you use a tea bag?

_____

When we put some sugar in the tea, it seems to disappear.

c. What is the scientific word for what happens to the sugar?

_____

1

3

1

Sc3

1

You use a spoon to stir the sugar
into your tea.

c. Write down why a metal spoon would feel warmer than a plastic one
when you stir your tea.

Sc3 ◯
1

_____

5 **The Moon**

There is a full Moon shining. Its position at 8 o'clock in the evening is shown
on the picture.

a. Draw the shadow of the boy on the picture.

◯
1

_____

b. On the picture, draw where the Moon will be seen at 12 o'clock,
midnight.

◯
1

_____

c. If the boy came back 14 days later and stood in the same place and at
the same time, what would he see?

Sc4 ◯
1

_____

d. How long does it take for the Moon to orbit the Earth?

_____

The Sun gives out light. It is said to be luminous. The Moon is not luminous.

e. Explain why we see the Moon as a bright object in the sky.

_____

_____

○ 1

○ Sc4
2

6 **The pond**

Here are some living things found in a pond. Their job in the food chain is given.

Pond weed

Stickleback

Tadpole

Mould

Secondary consumer

Primary consumer

Reducer

Producer

a. Draw the food chain that links these living things.

```
┌─────────────────────────────────────────────┐
│                                               │
│                                               │
│                                               │
│                                               │
│                                               │
└─────────────────────────────────────────────┘
```

b. How do the producers get their food?

_____

_____

Pond weed, sticklebacks, mould and tadpoles are all living things.

c. What **three** life processes do all these living things have in common?

_____

_____

_____

○ 1

○ 2

○ Sc3
3

7 **Circuits**

Here are the parts you would use to make a circuit that will light up a bulb.

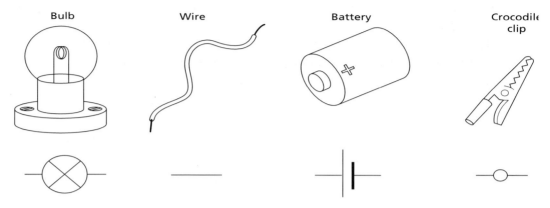

Underneath each drawing is the symbol that is used to draw that part in a circuit.

    a. Draw a diagram to show how you would put these together to make the bulb light up.

The symbol for a switch is —o⁀o— .

    b. Draw a second diagram to show where you would put a switch to turn the bulb on and off. Show the switch in the ON position.

Sc4

2

1

8 **Soil**

Mark and Jane want to find out which soil is best to use for planting their seeds. Their teacher said that the best soil is one that does not need watering very often.

They took four pots and filled each one with a different soil. They poured on some water and measured how long it took for the water to just start to run out of the hole at the bottom of the pot.

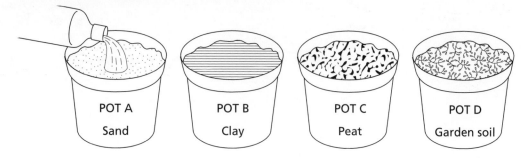

	Type of soil	Time for water to pass through
POT A	Sand	45 seconds
POT B	Clay	4 minutes 15 seconds
POT C	Peat	2 minutes 30 seconds
POT D	Garden soil	2 minutes

a. Which soil would be the best to use for their seeds?

_____

b. Why do you think this?

_____

c. Write down **two** things Mark and Jane could do to make their experiment a fair test.

_____

_____

d. How do plants get the goodness (nutrients) from the soil?

_____

1

Sc2

1

Sc1

2

Sc2

1

9 **Straw pipes**

You can make a pipe from a drinking or art straw by flattening the end and cutting it like this. It is played by blowing through the cut end.

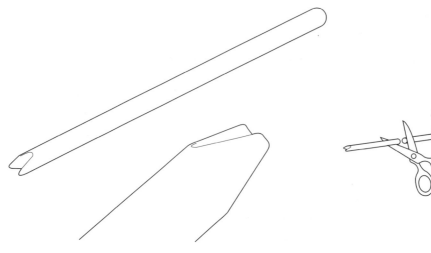

a. Why does the cut end make a sound when it is blown?

_____

b. What will happen if you cut the straw in half and blow again?

_____

c. How could you make the sound louder?

_____

d. Explain how you can hear the straw pipe playing.

_____

_____

_____

1

1

1

Sc4

3

TOTAL

INSTRUCTIONS

Read this carefully

Answers

Write your answers on the lines provided.

For some questions you may need to draw an answer, for others you simply put a tick or cross in the correct box(es).

You have 35 minutes to complete this test.

TEST 2

1 **Skeletons**

Here is a picture of a female skeleton.

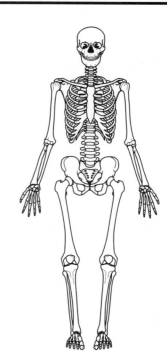

a. On the picture, draw and label three arrows:

Arrow A pointing to the part of the skeleton that protects the heart.

Arrow B pointing to the part that protects the brain.

Arrow C pointing to the part that can cradle a baby.

b. Apart from protection, what other **two** jobs does the skeleton do?

1. _____

2. _____

Muscles are joined to parts of the skeleton.

c. What job do muscles do?

_____

2 **Change**

Some materials change when they are heated. When they cool down again they change back to what they were like before. Other materials change when they are heated, but do not change back when they cool down. They remain changed forever.

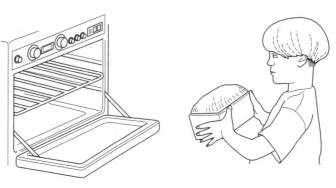

3

1

1

Sc2

2

a. For the changes listed below, put a tick in the box if you think the material can change back after heating or not.

		Can change back	Cannot change back
A	Damp clay heated in a kiln to make a pot	☐	☐
B	Iron heated in a blacksmith's furnace to make a horseshoe	☐	☐
C	Sand heated in an oven to make glass	☐	☐
D	Dough heated in an oven to make bread	☐	☐
E	Water heated in a kettle to make steam	☐	☐

These materials need different temperatures to make them change. Sand is heated to 1400°C, iron to 1500°C and dough is heated to 180°C.

b. What does °C mean?

_____

c. At what temperature does water change into steam?

_____

3 **Roller blades**

Kim has been given a pair of roller blades for her birthday. She is playing with Adam who gently pushes her from behind.

a. On the picture, draw an arrow to show the direction in which Kim moves.

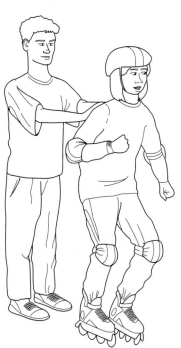

5

2

Sc3
2

Sc4
1

Kim now pushes against Adam who is standing still.

b. On the picture, draw an arrow to show the direction she moves now.

When Kim skates on the grass, she goes more slowly than on the pavement.

c. What is the force that slows her down called?

_____

d. On the picture, draw an arrow to show the direction of the force which slows her down.

When she skates on a slope, she moves down without having to push with her feet.

e. On the picture, draw an arrow which shows the direction of the force that is pulling her down the slope.

f. What is this force called?

_____

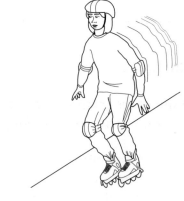

4 **Guessing game**

Rashni and Sarah are playing a guessing game. Rashni is looking at some pictures of living and non-living things. Sarah asks questions to find out which picture Rashni is looking at.

Sc4

a. Which **one** question would Sarah ask to find out if the picture is of a living thing?

Tick **one** box

A   Is it shiny or dull? ☐

B   Does it move? ☐

C   Is it heavy or light? ☐

D   Can it reproduce itself? ☐

E   Can it make its own food? ☐

b. Which extra question could Sarah ask to find out if the living thing is an animal?

_____

c. Which question would tell her that the living thing is a plant?

_____

d. Which question would tell her that the picture was of a metal?

_____

○ 1

○ 1

○ 1

○ Sc2

○ 1

5 Torch

Karl shines his torch at the mirror on his wall.

Mirror

D

A

B

C

a. At which place, A, B, C or D, would he see the spot of light?

_____

○ Sc4

1

b. Underline the word that best describes what happens to the light when it shines against the mirror?

deflected   bounced   reflected   detected

Karl now uses his torch to make shadows on the wall. He puts pieces of wood, glass and cloudy plastic in front of the torch.

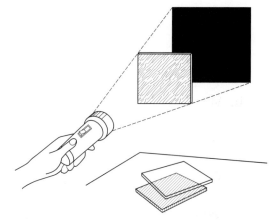

c. Which material makes the best shadow?

_____

d. Write down the reason for this.

_____

e. Karl is looking at his torch, which is switched off. Which diagram shows how he sees the torch? (The arrows show the direction taken by the rays of light.)

_____

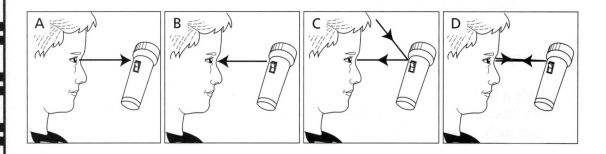

6 Teeth

If you use a dental mirror to look inside your mouth, you will see this.

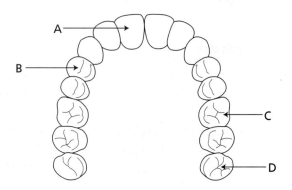

1

1

1

Sc4
1

a. Write down the names given to the teeth labelled A, B, C and D.

A _____

B _____

C _____

D _____

b. Write down the jobs that teeth A and D do.

A _____

D _____

c. What is the best thing to do every day to keep your teeth healthy?

                                                      Tick **one** box

Brush them once a day   ☐

Brush them after meals   ☐

Chew gum after meals   ☐

Rinse your mouth with mouthwash   ☐

Eat with your mouth closed   ☐

Eat an apple after meals   ☐

7 Celery

Inside a plant, water is carried through very thin tubes. If you cut across the stem of a plant such as celery you can see these tubes.

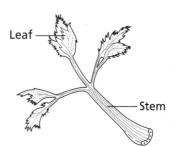
Leaf —
Stem —

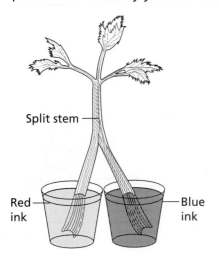
Split stem —
Red ink —
Blue ink —

In an experiment the bottom part of the stem of a piece of celery was split down the middle. Each half was placed in a pot of water. In one pot the water was coloured with red ink, in the other with blue ink. The celery was left for 3 hours.

4

2

Sc2
1

a. What did the celery leaves look like after 3 hours?

_____

Here is a drawing of the stem
which has been cut across.

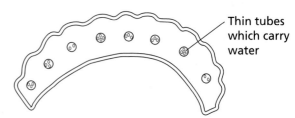

Thin tubes
which carry
water

b. What would you expect to see?

_____

Celery plants that grow in the garden have deep green leaves. Most of the
celery that you buy in the shops has very pale green or even white leaves.

c. Why does the celery from the shop have such pale leaves?

_____

d. Why does a celery plant need leaves?

_____

8 **Water**

Water can be found as liquid water, solid ice and steam which is a vapour.

a. From these words, choose those which complete the sentences about
water:

melts   cool   heat   condenses   evaporates   freezes   liquid

When you _____ ice it _____ to form liquid water.

When you _____ water vapour it _____
to form liquid water.

If you _____ liquid water, the water _____
to form water vapour.

If you cool _____ water it _____ and forms solid ice.

b. How are clouds formed?

_____

c. How does the water vapour in clouds form liquid rain?

_____

2

2

2

Sc3

1

TOTAL

Read this carefully

Answers

Write your answers on the lines provided.

For some questions you may need to draw an answer, for others you simply put a tick or cross in the correct box(es).

You have 35 minutes to complete this test.

TEST 3

1 **Taking your pulse**

The children in Class 3 are finding out what happens to their pulses when they do PE.

a. On the drawing of the hand and wrist, draw an X on the place where it is easy to find a pulse.

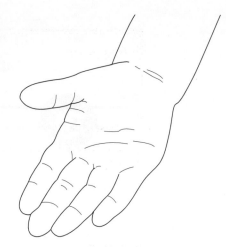

The children took their pulses and found that most had a count of about 70 beats every minute. After running 10 times round the hall, they measured their pulses again.

b. What do you think their new pulse counts would be?

Put a tick in **one** box

There is no pulse ☐

The pulse is slower ☐

The pulse is the same ☐

The pulse is faster ☐

1

c. Explain why it is that you can feel a pulse in your hand and wrist.

_____

_____

_____

_____

Sc2

4

2 **Forces**

Here is a drawing of a car driving along a flat and level road. The arrows show the direction of some of the forces that affect the movement of the car.

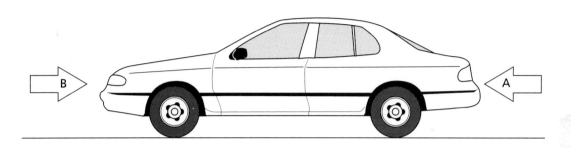

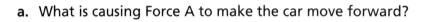

a. What is causing Force A to make the car move forward?

_____

b. What could be causing Force B, which slows the car down?

_____

c. For each of these sentences which describe the movement of the car, put a tick in **one** box which describes how the forces are working.

	Force A is the same as Force B	Force A is greater than Force B	Force B is greater than Force A
The car is not moving			
The car is slowing down			
The car is speeding up			
The car is moving at a steady speed			

1

2

Sc4

4

3 **Muscles**

This drawing shows the muscles
that work the bones of the leg
and make it move.

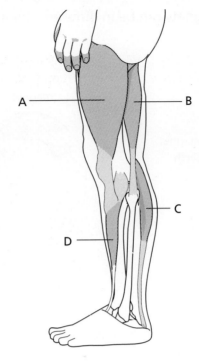

a. Which two muscles make the leg bend at the knee?
Write A and B, A and D, C and D or B and C

_____

1

b. Which two muscles lift the foot up and down?
Write A and D, A and C, C and D or B and C

_____

1

c. What do we call the places in the body where bones join, e.g. knee?

_____

1

The skeleton is used for moving the body.

d. Give **two** other reasons why the skeleton is important to humans.

1. _____

2. _____

Sc2

2

4 **Using magnets**

A lot of money can be earned from old cola cans. First they must be sorted
into those made of steel and those made of aluminium.

a. Why might you use a magnet to sort these cans?

_____

Sc4

1

Magnets can be in different shapes. All magnets have north and south poles.

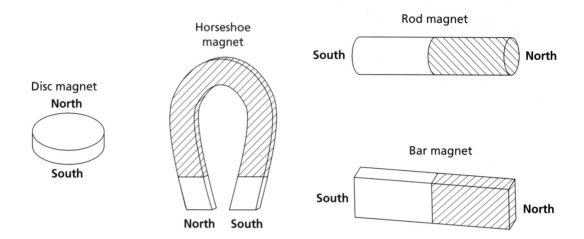

Here are some facts about magnets when they are held near to each other and other things.

	North pole of bar magnet	South pole of bar magnet
Steel paper clip	Attracts	Attracts
North pole of a horseshoe magnet	Repels	Attracts
South pole of a rod magnet	Attracts	Repels
10 pence piece	Does not attract	Does not attract

b. Fill in the words that are missing from these sentences about magnets?

Like poles _____ each other.

Unlike poles _____ each other.

c. Explain what is happening to the disc magnets in this drawing.

_____

_____

_____

_____

2

2

5 Day and night

The Moon moves round the Earth. The Earth moves round the Sun. The Earth and the Moon spin around.

a. Match these movements with the time each one takes by putting a tick in the correct box.

	24 hours	365 days	28 days	24 days
The time it takes for the Earth to spin on its axis				
The time it takes for the Moon to orbit the Earth				
The time it takes for the Earth to orbit the Sun				

b. On this drawing of the Sun, Earth and Moon, shade the part of the Earth where it is night.

c. Draw arrows on the picture to explain how we see moonlight.

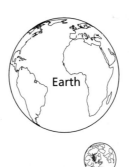

6 Materials

Look at this drawing of a plastic kettle. There is a reason for making each part of the kettle from a different material.

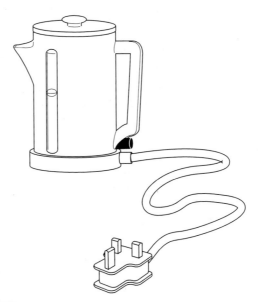

3

1

Sc4

1

Answer each question by underlining your choice from the answers given.

Question: What is the handle made of?

Answer: Metal   Plastic   Rubber

Question: Why is the handle made of this?

Answer: It is a good heat conductor It is a good heat insulator It is tough

Question: What is the flex made of?

Answer: Plastic   Plastic and metal   Metal

Question: Which part of the flex conducts electricity?

Answer: Plastic   Plastic and metal   Metal

Question: At what temperature does the water boil in the kettle?

Answer: 0 °C   100 °C   212 °C

Sc3 ⃝
5

7 Food

Class 6 visited a local field study centre. Each group had to go into the woodland to find out what one animal eats. Here is what each group found:

Group 1   Earthworms eat dead leaves.

Group 2   Hedgehogs eat insects, roots and berries.

Group 3   Moles eat earthworms.

Group 4   Caterpillars eat leaves.

Group 5   Sparrowhawks eat small birds.

Group 6   Rabbits eat leaves and grass.

Group 7   Blue tits eat caterpillars and small insects.

When they returned to the centre, they drew a food chain.

a. Complete the food chain. Either draw in the three empty boxes below or write the names underneath the boxes.

Sc2 ⃝
3

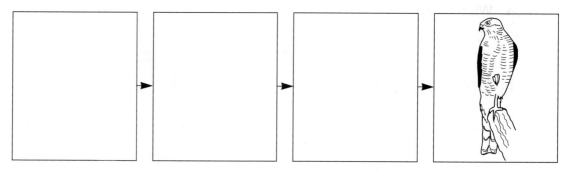

_____   _____   _____   Sparrowhawk

b. Plants are producers in a food chain. Explain what a producer is.

_____

_____

Sc2

4

8 **Hardness**

Some children are trying to find out which wood is the hardest. They used a hammer to knock in a nail, and measured the length of the nail after it had been hit five times. Each group used a different kind of wood.

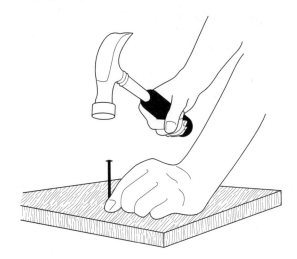

Here are their results:

Wood	Length of nail in centimetres (cm) sticking out of the wood
Oak	4.5
Redwood	2.5
Pine	3.0
Beech	4.0
Cedar	3.5

a. Which wood is the hardest?

_____

b. Explain how you know which wood is the softest?

_____

_____

1

Sc3

2

At the end of the lesson, the children talked about how fair the test was.

c. Put ticks by the suggestions you think would help to make the test fair
next time.

Some nails might be sharper than others,
use the same type of nails ☐

Some children are stronger than others,
use the same child to do the test ☐

Some hammers are heavier than others,
use the same hammer each time ☐

Some children had more practice than others,
let the children practice first ☐

Some children are better at hammering than others,
use the same child each time ☐

The nails are not all the same size,
use the same nails each time ☐

Sc3 +
Sc1
⬤
6

TOTAL

Life processes Level 3

1 **a** move **b** they produce; they grow
  c take in water; stay in sunlight
2 **a** they all grow in size; they are all eaten
  b moves from place to place; eats food
  c makes its own food

Life processes Level 4

1 move; breathe; feed; get rid of waste
2 They produce; They make their own food;
  They grow
3 drink water; eat food

Life processes Level 5

1 Feature: excrete; growth
  Meaning: move from place to place
  Animals: no; yes   Plants: yes; no; yes
2 N; D; N; D; D; L; N; N; L; D

Humans as organisms Level 3

1 **a** She does not clean her teeth often
  b Simon cleaned his teeth more often than Justin
2 **a** cheese and meat or nuts **b** nuts and bread
  or chapati **c** apple and orange or mango
  d sugar and cola
3 **a**

  b 100 heartbeats every minute
4 **a**

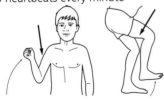

  b bones/skeleton
5 Too many tablets can harm/hurt you

Humans as organisms Level 4

1 **a** molars = grind food; incisors = cut food;
  canines = tear bits off food
  b brush your teeth after meals; drink milk; visit
  the dentist regularly
2 Part A lungs; Part B heart; Part C small intestine;

Part D kidney
3 stomach; small intestine; large intestine
4 **a** blood **b** arteries and veins
  c the more exercise the faster the heartbeat
5 puberty, adults, egg, foetus, baby, milk, child

Humans as organisms Level 5

1 **a** the greater/more the amount of fluoride the
  less tooth decay
  b 1 use toothpaste with fluoride; 2 clean teeth
  after meals/every day; 3 do not eat sugary food
2 **a** any three from cheese, milk, sardines, pilchards,
  chocolate
  b Menu B
3 **a** 1 = L (vein returning blood from lungs)
    2 = M (main artery taking blood to body)
    3 = V (Ventricle)
    4 = A (Auricle)
  b resting **c** 170 **d** 20 seconds
4 A = digestion of food B = storing sugar
  C = pumping blood around the body
  D = breathing air in and out
5 **a** 8.5 – 9.5 hours **b** about 1 hour **c** yes

Green plants as organisms Level 3

1 in a dark cupboard; on a sunny window ledge
2 dish A
3 the leaf veins would look red
4 **a** sycamore **b** ash **c** sycamore
5 the longer it takes to fall the further it will fly
  through the air

Green plants as organisms Level 4

1 **a** harder **b** it anchors/holds the plant in the soil
  c they take in water
2 **a** the geraniums in the cold barn
  b the geraniums in the warm dark barn
  c No, the leaves will be yellow/white
3 **a** Part A stamen, Part B stigma, Part C ovary,
  Part D petal **b** B-seeds germinate, C-new plant
  grows, D-flower forms, E-flower is pollinated,
  F-seed disperses
4 **a** buttercups **b** clover, nettles and vetch
  c they collect/drink nectar/sugar
  d they carry pollen (from one flower to another)

Plants as organisms Level 5

1 1. water, 2. light, 3. temperature
2 **a** 1. turn blue 2. do not turn blue
  b the leaves/need light to make starch/food
3 **a** the leaves **b** 1. to get/take in water from the
  soil 2. to get/take in nutrients/minerals from the
  soil **c** to anchor the plant/hold plant in the soil

4 A = stamen/anther; produces pollen
B = petal; attracts insects   C = leaf; makes food
for the plant   D = fruit/strawberry; attracts
animals for seed dispersal

Variation and classification Level 3

1 A = shellduck   B = oyster catcher
C = avocet   D = snipe   E = curlew

Variation and classification Level 4

1 A = topshell   B = scallop   C = limpet
D = mussel   E = whelk   F = razor shell

Variation and classification Level 5

1 A = oak   B = ash   C = plane   D = beech
E = elm   F = horse chestnut

Living things in their environment Level 3

1 **a**
Part	Helps it to
1 fins	swim
2 tail	swim
3 gill	breathe

b It makes it streamlined/helps it cut through
water

2 **a** Pond: newt, frog, pondweed, water snail
Soil: worm, bluebell, woodlouse; snail,
centipede
Sea: starfish, mussel, seaweed, crab
Air: owl, woodpecker, butterfly
b They all have wings/they are light

3 **a** B   **b** It has big tearing teeth

Living things in their environment Level 4

1 Producers: *any three from* small seaweed, plant
plankton, green seaweed, wood
First consumers: *any three from* periwinkle,
shrimp, animal plankton, ragworm, gribble
Second consumers: *any three from* herring gull,
anemone, mackerel, humans, flounder, octopus,
heron

2 **a** oak   **b** *any two from* beetle, shrew, snake, fox
c eat food; breathe; get rid of waste

3 **a** short-tailed voles   **b** 1. sharp/hooked beak
2. sharp claws/talons 3. good eyesight/large eyes

Living things in their environment Level 5

1 1. not enough light/water for grass to grow
2. too much wear by feet/boots
3. rabbits cannot get inside and eat grass

2 **a** flat lichen   **b** 8 kilometres/km
c count lichen in a given area/use quadrant; count
the first 20 (*any number greater than 10*) lichens
that you find

3 **a** 1. blue/purple petals attract bees/insects
2. they need/can live with little light
b 1. They can fly 2. They have sharp beaks to
catch insects   **c** They decay/rot the leaves
d They can cause disease

Materials and their properties
Grouping and classifying materials Level 3

1 Group A They are metals; Group 2 They are all
wood/wooden; Group 3 They are plastics
2 1c   2a   3b
3 **a** D, E   **b** A, B, C   **c** glass   **d** transparent
4 *link* tyre - rubber - flexible   slate - roof - waterproof
cork - tile - warm   brass - plug - conducts
electricity
5 **a** foam polystyrene   **b** use the same amount of
drink each time
6 **a** diamond   **b** chalk

Grouping and classifying materials Level 4

1 **a** calcite, gypsum and talc   **b** diamond,
corundum, topaz   **c** apatite
2 **a** Solid: butter, paper, glass, ice, sugar
Liquid: petrol, cola, oil, syrup
Gas: air, steam, carbon, dioxide
b

Property	Solid	Liquid	Gas
Can flow through a tube or pipe		✔	✔
Keeps its own shape	✔		
Is usually rigid or stiff	✔		
Can be squashed into a small space			✔
Fills the shape of the container		✔	✔

3 a & b

	Does not conduct heat	See-through	Hard	Easy to bend	Waterproof
Drinking glass		✔	✔		✔
Plastic mug	✔		✔		✔
Plastic clingfilm		✔		✔	✔
Wooden spoon	✔		✔		✔
Aluminium foil	✔		✔	✔	✔
Oven gloves	✔			✔	

4 Steel – Stronger and harder
Solder – Melts at lower temperature
Bronze – Hard, easier to cast
Stainless steel – Resists rusting
Brass – Harder, more attractive

5 **a** B **b** B loses less heat than A or C **c** insulator
d 1. use the same amount of water 2. use the same type of teapot 3. leave the cosies on for the same amount of time

6 **a** nylon ruler **b** 1. keep the length the same 2. keep the thickness the same 3. keep the width the same **c** wooden ruler; it takes more/most force to bend it

Grouping and classifying materials Level 5

1 **a** iron **b** lead **c** Yes, Yes, Yes **d** Would not be attracted: copper, brass, lead, aluminium; Would be attracted: iron, nickel

e

	North pole	South pole
North pole	repels	attract
South pole	attract	repels

2 **a** *tick* aluminium, brass, steel, copper, cobalt metal
cross polythene, wood, perspex
b insulators **c** it is not metal/all other are metal
d carbon brushes in motor, carbon filament light bulbs, carbon resistors, carbon and zinc batteries

3 **a** Rock A = malachite/copper ore
Rock B = quartz Rock C = galena/lead ore
b They all contain metal **c** It would attract/stick to heamatite/iron ore **d** igneous, it has crystals

4 *choice of plastic* perspex; PVC; polystyrene; polythene
why chosen does not bend, does not break easily; easy to cut, bends; does not bend, cannot be cut; bends easily, tears easily

5 **a**

	Oak	Copper	Nylon
Can be cut with knife	Yes	No	Yes
Can push in drawing pin	No	No	Yes
Attracted to magnet	No	No	No
Conducts electricity	No	Yes	No
Rings when dropped	No	Yes	No
Can be beaten into flat sheets	No	Yes	No
Can be made into a thread	No	Yes	Yes
Looks shiny when cut	No	Yes	No
Burns when lit	Yes	No	No
Melts when heated	No	No	No
Floats in water	Yes	No	Yes

b copper
c oak

Changing material Level 3

1 *reversible* ice lollies ... soup ... butter ...
2 **a** It would disappear/dissolve **b** It would disappear/evaporate **c** It would melt

d 1. It would freeze; 2. The water/it would expand/get bigger/would break the bottle
e The steam would condense/turn back to water/water would run down the window

3 *Things which melt when they are warmed:* chocolate, margarine
Things which burn in a candle flame: cocktail sticks, paper, cork
Things which do not change when they are warmed: vinegar, salt, cooking oil

4 **a**
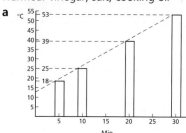

b a thermometer **c** degrees Celsius **d** It would heat up more quickly

Changing material Level 4

1 *Condensation = near/next to cloud over mountain Evaporation = close to surface of the sea/lake*
2 **a** the air **b** condensation
c On the outside of a cold drink on a hot day; On the windows inside the car on a cold morning; On a bathroom mirror
3 **a** It had evaporated **b** It dissolved **c** Ipswich
d 1. Used the same amount of water each time 2. Put the dishes in the same place 3. Used clean bottles for each sample
4 1. boils, 100°C, evaporates, condenses
2. 0 °C, freezes, thermometer
3. melts, liquid

Changing material Level 5

1 A N because the wax is forming carbon dioxide and water
B R because jelly goes liquid when heated
C R because water can be reheated to form steam
D N because the match burns to form carbon dioxide and water
E N because hard clay cannot take in water and change back to soft clay
F N because gas burns to form carbon dioxide and water

2 **a** getting warmer - still solid ice **b** It is melting
c liquid/water **d** reaches maximum; reaches room temperature
3 **a** heat/energy from the Sun **b** clouds **c** rain
d slows it down/stops it **e** gravity
4 **a** It evaporates
b 1. wind/more wind 2. heat/hot weather
3. how big it is/size to start with
c *pupils should draw a similar curve underneath the one on the graph/pupils should draw new curve cutting time axis before 11.00*

d puddle evaporates faster/more quickly

e it dries up/no water left/puddle has gone

Separating mixtures of materials Level 3

1 **a** Heavy: yellow layer, black layer Light: pale brown layer, dark brown layer

b Would pass through the sieve: pale brown layer, dark brown layer, yellow layer

Would not pass through sieve: black layer

2 **a** silk/closely woven cloth/one with the smallest holes

b It/mud stays on the cloth

c It is still salty/contains salt

d Boil the muddy water and collect the steam

3 Alka Seltzer tablet, sugar lump, grains of salt

Separating mixtures of materials Level 4

1 **a** the grounds are too big/the holes/pores in the paper are too small

b filtered it

c tea leaves from tea, sand and water

2 **a** 1. stir it 2. use hot water **b** evaporate the water and collect the powder from the dish

3 **a** soluble: the coffee granules, the sugar insoluble: the cup, the biscuit, the spoon

b There is less coffee in the solution/the coffee is more dilute

c Stir the milk/heat up the milk

Separating mixtures of materials Level 5

1 **a** river bank **b** The sample has a lot of small particles/fine soil in sieves 3 and 4

c garden **d** lots of particles/fewer small particles

e Put the same amount of soil into the nest at the start

f

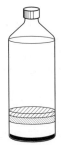

g They have lost water/dried out/evaporated

2 **a** 20 (*1 mark*) grams (*1 mark*)

b 16 (*1 mark*) grams (*1 mark*)

c 56 (*1 mark*) °C (*1 mark*)

d Only 40 grams would dissolve/some would fall to the bottom of the container

3 **a** 1d 2a 3e 4c 5b

b ... insoluble materials from liquids

c Let the mixture settle (*1 mark*) then carefully pour off the water. (*1 mark*) *Give an extra mark for the expression 'decant liquid'.*

Physical processes
Electricity Level 3

1 One crocodile clip is not connected

2 C, D

3 The more bulbs the dimmer they are/she had more bulbs

Electricity Level 4

1 **a** C **b** A **c** B

2 **a** both **b** both

3 **a** B **b** E

Electricity Level 5

1 **a** B **b** It is smaller/lower/decreases/down

2

Circuit	Only the buzzer is on	Only the bulb is on	Both the buzzer and bulb are on	The buzzer and bulb are both off
A				✔
B	✔			
C		✔		
D			✔	
E		✔		

Forces and motion Level 3

1 **a** the ring magnet **b** a north pole near to a north pole = push; a south pole near to a south pole = push; a south pole near to a north pole = pull

2 door spring = pulling; mattress spring = pushing; ball pen spring = pushing; kitchen scales spring = pushing; pin ball game spring = pulling

3 **a** Jane **b** Justin **c** How rough/smooth the mat is/friction

4 **a** It is rolling towards you = It goes more slowly *or* it stops rolling

It is rolling away from you = It goes more quickly

It is rolling across a table = It changes direction

Somebody is blowing from the other side (blow football) = It stops rolling

b Who blows the harder

Forces and motion Level 4

1 **a** The biggest one/the largest area/30 cm

b Gravity

c Air resistance/fiction

d 1. Dropped them from the same height

2. Keep the load/mass the same

2 **a** 1. Make sure the slope/height of ramps is the same 2. Let it travel the same distance

b Smooth plastic

c Friction

3 a

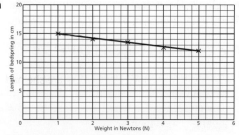

4 marks + 1 mark for best fit

b 16 cm

c *1 mark for arrow vertically downwards (gravity)*
+ 1 mark for arrow vertically upwards

4 The force of gravity on the soil C
The force of the man on the wheelbarrow handles B
The force of the ground on the wheel E

Forces and motion Level 5

1 a Rockets will stay in the bottle/nothing/stays
still/won't go up/will not move
b Rocket will stay in the bottle/nothing/stays
still/won't go up/will not move
c Rocket will take off/go up
d Newtons
e Grams

2 a

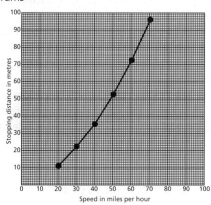

b 62/63 metres
c The tyres will not grip so well
d The road surface/what the road is made of
(*1 mark*) The tread/surface of the tyre (*1 mark*)
e *Weight of car down ↓ and reaction of road up ↑*

3 force of 39500 N = Does not move force of
20500 N = Sinks force of 40000 N = Rises

4 A *movement* The yacht moves forward (*1 mark*)
forces wind, water resistance, water friction
(*2 marks*)
B *movement* The yacht slows down/stops (*1 mark*)
forces wind, current, water resistance, water friction
(*2 marks*)
C *movement* The yacht speeds up/starts to move
again (*1 mark*)

forces wind, current, motor, water resistance,
water friction (*2 marks*)
D *movement* The yacht speeds up/goes faster (*1
mark*)
forces wind, water friction, motor (*2 marks*)

Light and sound Level 3

1 The foil reflects light
2 a Sue **b** The light cannot pass through the
cardboard/the light can only pass through the hole
3 a Group C
  b Sound/whistle becomes fainter/quieter/softer
the further they are from the whistle
  c Blow louder/move to the middle/nearer
4 C
5 a It jumps/moves up and down
  b The harder he hits the higher the rice jumps

Light and sound Level 4

1

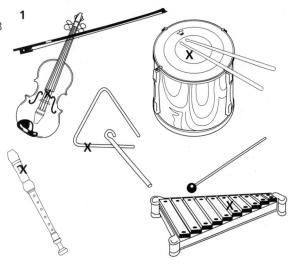

2 a No (*1 mark*) because some materials/things
carry sound better than others (*1 mark*)
  b Keep the length of the string/wire/line the same
3 a A to E
  b 1. Move near to the screen 2. Move the
projector further from the screen
  c Light will not pass through the head/the head
stops the light/light travels in a straight line/light
cannot bend round the head
4 a *Mirrors arranged so that reflect light in general
direction of Wall A = 1 mark*
  b *Light drawn so that angles of incidence and
reflection are correct = 1 mark*

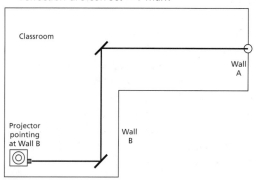

Light and sound Level 5

1 **a** Triangle
b *Pupils should draw incident ray from triangle and reflected ray to eye at same angle to the perpendicular (1 mark). Pupils should draw an arrow showing light coming **from** the object **to** the eye (1 mark)*

2 **a** D
b Tighten the string/use thinner string
c pluck the string harder
d They vibrate (*1 mark*) and make the air vibrate (*1 mark*). The air makes part of the ear vibrate (*1 mark*)

3 1d 2a 3c 4e 5b

4 *true* D, E *false* A, B, C

The Earth and beyond Level 3

1 **a**

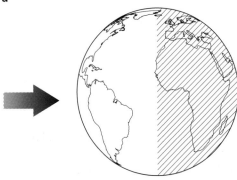

b *True* B, D *False* A, C

2 **a** 1. The shadow moves 2. The shadow gets shorter then longer
b The Sun appears to move (*1 mark*) across the sky (*1 mark*)

3 **a**

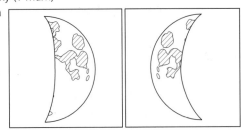

The Earth and beyond Level 4

1 1c 2d 3b 4a

2 reflects, Sun, reflects, Sun

3 **a**

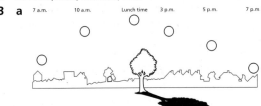

7 a.m. 10 a.m. Lunch time 3 p.m. 5 p.m. 7 p.m.

b at 12.00/lunchtime

4 **a** *Circle Dec drawn below Sun in picture*
b *Circle Jun drawn above the Sun in picture*

The Earth and beyond Level 5

1 correct order = (A) C H D F E B G
(A = full moon) C = gibbous H = first quarter
D = crescent F = new E = crescent B = last quarter G = gibbous

2 **a** *Diagram/description to show the Earth spinning on its axis and turning once a day*
b *Diagram/description of how half the Earth is in sunlight, the other half in darkness*
c *Diagram/description of how it takes the Earth 1 year to orbit the Sun*
d *Description/diagram of how the Earth is tilted on its axis and parts are near the Sun*
e *Description/diagrams to show how the Sun lights up the Moon and we see the sunlit part*
f *Description of how the Moon does not rotate at the same time as the Earth*

Test 1

1 **a** Anther **b** Stigma **c** To attract insects **d** Ovary

2 strawberry flower = W St John's Wort = Y
primrose = X violet = Z

3 **a** Brand E **b** Brand D **c** Stop smoking/do not smoke

4 **a** gas = steam/bubbles liquid = water solid = kettle
b The tea bag strains/filters it
c Dissolve(s)
d Metal is a better conductor than plastic

5 **a** and **b**

c He would see a new moon/no Moon
d 28 days
e The light from the Sun is reflected by the surface of the Moon

6 **a** Producer → Primary consumer → Secondary consumer → Reducer *or*
Pondweed → Tadpole → Stickleback → Mould
b They make their own food/by photosynthesis/ from carbon dioxide, water and sunlight
c nutrition/feeding; growth; reproduction

7 a

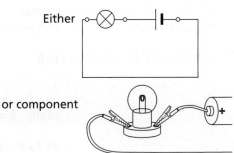

Either

or component

b

Switch anywhere
in the circuit

8 a Clay/Pot B
b Water takes longest to pass through
c 1. Use same amount of water
   2. Use same amount of soil
d Through their roots

9 a It/the end vibrates
b The sound/note becomes higher
c Blow harder
d Vibrations make the air vibrate (*1 mark*) and vibrations travel through the air (*1 mark*). Also the ear/ear drum vibrates (*1 mark*)

Test 2

1 a A = sternum   B = skull   C = pelvis
b 1. Helps us move/movement
   2. Supports the body
c Move (*1 mark*) bones (*1 mark*)

2 a *Can change back* B, E   *Cannot change back* A, C, D
b Degrees (*1 mark*) Celsius (*1 mark*)
c 100 (*1 mark*) °c (*1 mark*)

3 a

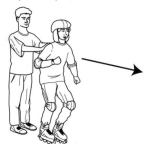

b

c Friction
d

e

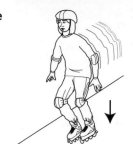

f Gravity

4 a D   **b** B   **c** E   **d** A

5 a B   **b** reflected   **c** wood
d Light will not pass through it/the wood stops the light/it is opaque
e C

6 a A = incisors   B = canines   C = premolars
D = molar
b A cut up food   D grind up/crush food
c Brush them after meals

7 a Some leaves were red, some blue
b Some tubes red, some blue
c It has been kept in the dark
d To make food/nutrition/photosynthesis

8 a heat, melts, cool, condenses, heat, evaporates, liquid, freezes
b Water evaporates (*1 mark*) from rivers/sea (*1 mark*) to form water vapour
c The water condenses

Test 3

1 a

b The pulse is faster
c The heart (*1 mark*) pumps blood (*1 mark*) through the arteries (*1 mark*) in pulses (*1 mark*)

2 a The engine
b Air/air resistance (*1 mark*), friction (*1 mark*)
c The car is not moving = Force A is the same as Force B
The car is slowing down = Force B is greater than Force A
The car is speeding up = Force A is greater than Force B
The car is moving at a steady speed = Force A is greater than Force B

3 **a** A and B
   b C and D
   c Joint(s)
   d 1. Gives support/stand upright/prevents collapse
      2. Protects the body/makes blood

4 **a** Steel cans are attracted/stick to magnet
   b repel; attract
   c The poles of each magnet repel (*1 mark*) the like poles (*1 mark*) of the one above and below

5 **a** Earth to spin on its axis = 24 hours
     Moon to orbit the earth = 28 days
     Earth to orbit the Sun = 365 days
   b and **c**

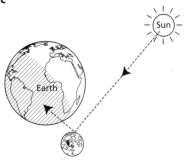

6 **a** Plastic
   b It is an insulator
   c Plastic and metal
   d Metal
   e 100 °C

7 **a** *should draw or write* leaves; caterpillars; blue tits
   b Producers use sunlight (*1 mark*) to make their own food (*1 mark*) which is eaten (*1 mark*) by consumers (*1 mark*)

8 **a** Oak
   b Redwood (*1 mark*) because nail went in furthest (*1 mark*)
   c *should tick all*